INTERSCIENCE TRACTS ON PHYSICS AND ASTRONOMY

Edited by R. E. Marshak
University of Rochester

1. **D. J. Hughes**
    NEUTRON OPTICS

2. **M. S. Livingston**
    HIGH-ENERGY ACCELERATORS

3. **L. Spitzer, Jr.**
    PHYSICS OF FULLY IONIZED GASES, second edition

4. **T. G. Cowling**
    MAGNETOHYDRODYNAMICS

5. **D. ter Haar**
    INTRODUCTION TO THE PHYSICS OF MANY-BODY SYSTEMS

6. **E. J. Öpik**
    PHYSICS OF METEOR FLIGHT IN THE ATMOSPHERE

7. **K. Mendelssohn**
    CRYOPHYSICS

8. **J. L. Delcroix**
    INTRODUCTION TO THE THEORY OF IONIZED GASES

9. **T. E. Sterne**
    AN INTRODUCTION TO CELESTIAL MECHANICS

10. **J. Weber**
    GENERAL RELATIVITY AND GRAVITATIONAL WAVES

11. **R. E. Marshak and E. C. G. Sudarshan**
    INTRODUCTION TO ELEMENTARY PARTICLE PHYSICS

12. **J. L. Olsen**
    ELECTRON TRANSPORT IN METALS

13. **M. Françon**
    MODERN APPLICATIONS OF PHYSICAL OPTICS

14. **P. B. Jones**
    THE OPTICAL MODEL IN NUCLEAR AND PARTICLE PHYSICS

Additional volumes in preparation

The Optical Model in Nuclear and Particle Physics

P. B. JONES

Nuclear Physics Laboratory
Oxford, England

1963
INTERSCIENCE PUBLISHERS
a division of John Wiley & Sons, New York • London

Preface

It is hoped that this book will give an introduction to the principles of the optical model of the nucleus. Chapter 1 contains a short account of the giant resonances, the theory of Feshbach, Porter, and Weisskopf, and the measurement of nuclear size. Chapter 2 discusses derivations of the model based on expansions of the scattering amplitude in powers of the strength of the nucleon-nucleon potential and on the dispersion formalisms for nuclear and potential scattering. Chapter 3 discusses the model at intermediate and high nucleon energies and the determination of nuclear structure. The system of units is such that $\hbar = c = 1$.

The content of the tract is restricted to elastic scattering. Distorted-wave calculations of more general nuclear reactions are not considered.

In accordance with the purpose of the book, it was decided not to present an extensive compilation of the results of existing optical model analyses. The list of references is therefore not complete.

I am most grateful for permission to use figures which have been published in conference reports and in journals. The source is given in each case.

I am very much indebted to Dr. A. M. Lane for his critical reading of the complete manuscript, and to Dr. A. B. Clegg, Dr. P. S. Fisher, Dr. P. E. Hodgson, and Dr. J. R. Rook for discussions on the contents of different chapters. The book was written during the tenure of a Research Fellowship at St. Catherine's College, given by the Central Electricity Generating Board.

Oxford, England, 1963   P. B. JONES

v

Contents

vii

CHAPTER 1

Introduction

1.1 Giant Resonances

An account of the optical model may be started by considering the elastic scattering of a neutron by a nucleus, that is, a scattering process in which the nucleus is left in its ground state. A model for this process in which the nucleus is represented by a real potential, of short range, depending only on the space coordinate of the incident neutron was investigated by Bethe (1935). The scattering cross section for such a potential, calculated as a function of neutron energy, passes through resonances with a spacing of the order of 10 Mev. The predicted capture cross section for the transition in which the neutron emits a photon and jumps to a bound state of the potential is both small and a slowly varying function of energy. Such a slow variation was obviously in disagreement with the slow neutron cross section measurements of Moon and Tillman (1935), Bjerge and Westcott (1935), and Szilard (1935). The capture cross sections were found to be at least as great as the elastic scattering cross sections and depended on the temperature of the medium used to moderate the neutrons so that a rapid variation with neutron energy could be inferred.

Breit and Wigner (1936) pointed out that the formation of excited states of the complete system, the compound nucleus comprising both the incident neutron and the nucleus, could give a qualitative explanation of the measured cross sections. The excited state would be unstable, the total energy width Γ and the neutron width Γ_n being in most cases less than 1 ev, so that the Breit-Wigner dispersion formula for the reaction cross section (Blatt and Weisskopf, 1952, p. 408)

$$\sigma_r = \frac{\pi}{k^2} \frac{\Gamma_n(\Gamma - \Gamma_n)}{(E - E_0)^2 + \Gamma^2/4} \qquad (1.1\text{-}01)$$

valid for $E \approx E_0$, would give a cross section having the observed rapid variation with energy. These ideas were also implicit in the compound nucleus or strong-coupling model of Bohr (1936). A rigorous basis for the dispersion theory of nuclear reactions was later provided by the work of Kapur and Peierls (1938), which is described in greater detail in Sections 2.4 and 2.5. The most important idea put forward by Breit and Wigner and by Bohr is that the fine structure observed in slow neutron cross sections is the result of the scattering process passing through intermediate states in which many nucleons are excited. The single particle model of Bethe would not therefore appear to be relevant.

However, Ford and Bohm (1950) examined the zero energy neutron total cross section as a function of mass number, A, and found some evidence for broad resonances, for which the compound nucleus model could give no reasonable explanation.

The measurement of fast neutron total cross sections in the energy range 0.1 to 3 Mev by Barschall (1952) and by Miller, Adair, Bockelman, and Darden (1952) gave similar results. When averaged to give a smooth variation with energy, the cross sections were found to have broad maxima with widths of the order of 1 Mev, the positions of which varied in a regular way with mass number. These maxima cannot be understood in terms of the compound nucleus model which predicts a monotonic decrease of the averaged total cross sections with energy. An explanation of the existence and positions of the maxima was provided by the optical model of the nucleus.

The central feature of the optical model is the representation of a nucleus by a potential which is a function of the space coordinate and energy of the incident particle only. The potential is complex, the imaginary part representing all inelastic processes

allowed by the selection rules for strong interactions and by con-
servation of energy (Bethe, 1940). Solution of the Schrödinger
equation for the incident particle interacting through the optical
model potential only, then leads to the differential and total
elastic scattering cross sections and the reaction cross section,
which is equal to the sum of the cross sections for all allowed
inelastic processes.

The dependence of the optical model potential on the coordinate and energy of the incident particle will be discussed in
Section 2.8. The most simple approximate form is the square
well potential

$$V(r) = U - iW \qquad r < R,$$
$$= 0 \qquad\qquad r > R, \qquad (1.1\text{-}02)$$

where **r** is the coordinate, in the centre of mass system, of the
incident particle. This is the form which was used by Ford and
Bohm (1950), Adair (1954), and Feshbach, Porter, and Weisskopf (1954) in their explanation of the maxima, which are now
known as giant resonances. Ford and Bohm, and Adair, calculated the zero energy neutron scattering cross section as a
function of mass number using the approximation $W = 0$. This
cross section, assuming a spherical nucleus, results from the
$l = 0$ partial wave and has resonances for values of U and R
such that

$$KR = (n - \tfrac{1}{2})\pi \qquad n = 1, 2, 3, \dots , \qquad (1.1\text{-}03)$$

where

$$K^2 = -2\,MU, \quad R = r_1 A^{1/3}, \qquad (1.1\text{-}04)$$

and M is the reduced mass of the neutron. The value of the
zero energy cross section for a given nucleus depends on the
fine structure already noted and it is therefore necessary to
average the measured cross section near zero energy. For $U =$
-42 Mev and $r_1 = 1.45 \times 10^{-13}$ cm, the $3s$ and $4s$ giant resonances ($n = 3, 4$) are predicted to appear at $A = 55$ and 151,

respectively, in fair agreement with the energy-averaged experimental cross sections. However, nuclei with mass numbers of about 150 are known to be nonspherical with the result that l is not a good quantum number and the simple analysis just presented is not correct in principle. A theory taking into account the nonspherical shape of these nuclei leads to improved agreement with experiment (see Section 2.6 and Figure 2). The positions of the giant resonances in fast neutron (0 to 3 Mev) total cross sections were successfully correlated by Feshbach, Porter, and Weisskopf, the parameters of the square well potential required being $U = -42$ Mev, $W = 1.26$ Mev, and $r_1 = 1.45 \times 10^{-13}$ cm. To summarise, the existence of the giant resonances together with the successful correlation of their positions provides clear evidence for the validity of the single particle or optical model in so far as energy-averaged cross sections are considered.

An earlier success of the optical model, however, had been the calculation of high energy neutron total cross sections as a function of mass number. For example, Fernbach, Serber, and Taylor (1949) were able to fit the measured total cross sections, at 90 Mev neutron energy, for a series of elements ranging from lithium to uranium, using a single complex square well potential. The mean free path between collisions for a neutron in nuclear matter, implied by the imaginary part of the potential, was found to be of the order of the radius of a light nucleus. This therefore explained the experimentally observed transparency, which means a reaction cross section much less than the value πR^2 predicted by the compound nucleus model at high energies. The possibility of such a limitation of the compound nucleus model at high energies had been suggested by Serber (1947).

For incident neutron beams of broad energy, the existence of the giant resonances implies a neutron mean free path (λ) in nuclear matter equal to at least several nuclear radii. Such a long mean free path is also necessary to explain the single-particle nature of the ground and low-lying excited states of many nuclei implied by the success of the shell model (see, for example, the review of Elliot and Lane, 1957). The explanation, first suggested by Weisskopf (1951), lies in the Fermi-Dirac statistics of the nucleons. The effect is most simply demonstrated by the elastic scattering of a neutron by a nucleus which is represented by a zero-temperature Fermi gas. The imaginary part of the optical model potential is, in this model, the result of collisions in which the incident neutron excites a nucleon to a state above the Fermi surface. The imaginary part of the potential is given by

$$W(r) = \tfrac{1}{2} \mid \mathbf{v} \mid \sigma \rho(r) = \tfrac{1}{2} \mid \mathbf{v} \mid / \lambda, \qquad (1.1\text{-}05)$$

where $\mid \mathbf{v} \mid$ is the relative velocity of the colliding nucleons, ρ is the nucleon density for the target nucleus, and σ is the effective total nucleon-nucleon cross section, averaged over neutrons and protons. The derivation of this formula is given in Section 2.3. Let us consider the example of a slow incident neutron and suppose that the average kinetic energy of nucleons in the nucleus is 25 Mev, and the nuclear radius $1.45A^{1/3} \times 10^{-13}$ cm. If there were no exclusion principle, the effective cross section would be approximately equal to the free cross section. This would result in an imaginary part $W \approx 45$ Mev and a mean free path $\lambda \approx 0.5 \times 10^{-13}$ cm. However, owing to the exclusion principle, only nucleons in states close to the Fermi surface may be excited in this way, and the effective cross section is very much less than the free cross section. The consequences of such a model were examined by Lane and Wandel (1955) who showed that it could account for the low value of W found by Feshbach, Porter, and Weisskopf. Equation 1.1-05 shows that this value of W implies a mean free path $\lambda \approx 2 \times 10^{-12}$ cm. Such a model represents a very rough approximation, but is sufficient to show the importance of the exclusion principle.

So far, only the circumstance in which the incident particle is a neutron has been considered. However, the optical model has been found to give a good account of the elastic scattering and reaction cross sections of protons with energies in the interval 2 to 300 Mev, and of heavier compound particles. The results are presented in Sections 3.2–3.5. The optical model has also been successfully used in atomic physics, for example, in the calculation of the elastic scattering of slow electrons by neutral atoms (Mittleman and Watson, 1959; Lippmann, Mittleman, and Watson, 1959).

A quantitative account of the procedure of averaging cross sections over intervals of energy and some necessary definitions are given in the following section. More complete discussions of the compound nucleus model are contained in the papers of Friedman and Weisskopf (1955), Lane and Thomas (1958), and Breit (1959).

1.2 The Gross Structure Problem

The relation between the gross structure problem, that is the prediction of cross sections averaged over intervals of energy, and the fine structure which actually obtains, can be made more clear by some definitions given by Feshbach, Porter, and Weisskopf (1954). As the inclusion of the Coulomb potential is not, at the moment, a necessary complication, the discussion of this section relates to the elastic scattering of neutrons. The neutron is assumed to have spin 0, an account of the effect of spin-orbit coupling being left until Section 3.2 is reached.

The asymptotic solution of the Schrödinger equation, satisfying the scattering boundary conditions is

$$\psi(\mathbf{r}) \sim \frac{\sqrt{\pi}}{kr} \sum_{l=0}^{\infty} (2l + 1)^{1/2}(i)^{l+1}\{e^{-i(kr-(1/2)\,l\pi)}$$

$$- S_l e^{i(kr-(1/2)\,l\pi)}\} Y_{l,0}(\theta) \quad (1.2\text{-}01)$$

(Blatt and Weisskopf, 1952, ch. 8), where k is the centre of mass momentum. The first term, containing e^{-ikr}, represents an ingoing spherical wave, and the second term an outgoing wave multiplied by the complex number S_l which is a function of k and represents the modification induced by the scattering interaction. S_l is related to the complex phase shift by $S_l = \exp(2i\delta_l)$. The cross sections (elastic and reaction) are completely determined by the S_l. The cross sections are

$$\sigma_s = \frac{\pi}{k^2} \sum_l (2l + 1) \mid 1 - S_l \mid^2 \qquad (1.2\text{-}02)$$

and

$$\sigma_r = \frac{\pi}{k^2} \sum_l (2l + 1)(1 - \mid S_l \mid^2). \qquad (1.2\text{-}03)$$

The total cross section is defined as the sum

$$\sigma_t = \sigma_s + \sigma_r. \qquad (1.2\text{-}04)$$

The fine structure of the cross sections for low energy neutrons implies that the S_l, as functions of k, are subject to sharp fluctuations. The average of a function $S_l(k)$ over some energy interval I is denoted by $\langle S_l \rangle$. The nature of the averaging procedure is not important in the present context but will be described in Section 2.6. The neutron centre of mass energy E will be assumed to be such that the inequality $D \ll I \ll E$ can be satisfied, where $D(E)$ is the average spacing between the energy levels of the compound nucleus. We refer, of course, only to the energy levels which can be formed from the neutron and the target nucleus. The average cross sections are obtained by application of the averaging procedure to equations 1.2-02 and 1.2-04. Thus,

$$\langle \sigma_s \rangle = \frac{\pi}{k^2} \sum_l (2l + 1)\langle \mid 1 - S_l \mid^2 \rangle. \qquad (1.2\text{-}05)$$

Averaging individual terms in the squared modulus gives

$$\langle \sigma_s \rangle = \frac{\pi}{k^2} \sum_l (2l + 1)\{\mid 1 - \langle S_l \rangle \mid^2 - \mid \langle S_l \rangle \mid^2 + \langle \mid S_l \mid^2 \rangle\}, \qquad (1.2\text{-}06)$$

and similarly

$$\langle \sigma_t \rangle = \frac{\pi}{k^2} \sum_l (2l + 1)\{\mid 1 - \langle S_l \rangle \mid^2 + 1 - \mid \langle S_l \rangle \mid^2\}. \qquad (1.2\text{-}07)$$

The condition $I \ll E$ permits the factor $1/k^2$ to be excluded from the averaging procedure. An interval I such that $I \gg D$ is clearly necessary if the averaging procedure is to be useful.

The compound elastic and shape elastic cross sections, σ_{ce} and σ_{se}, are defined by the relations

$$\langle \sigma_s \rangle = \sigma_{se} + \sigma_{ce} \qquad (1.2\text{-}08)$$

and

$$\sigma_{ce} = \frac{\pi}{k^2} \sum_l (2l + 1)\{\langle |S_l|^2 \rangle - |\langle S_l \rangle|^2\}. \qquad (1.2\text{-}09)$$

Comparing equations 1.2-06 and 1.2-09, it is seen that σ_{se} is the scattering cross section given by the averaged functions $\langle S_l \rangle$. The cross section for compound nucleus formation is defined by

$$\sigma_c = \frac{\pi}{k^2} \sum_l (2l + 1)\{1 - |\langle S_l \rangle|^2\}. \qquad (1.2\text{-}10)$$

From 1.2-07,

$$\langle \sigma_t \rangle = \sigma_{se} + \sigma_c , \qquad (1.2\text{-}11)$$

and

$$\langle \sigma_r \rangle = \sigma_c - \sigma_{ce} . \qquad (1.2\text{-}12)$$

At higher energies, the compound nucleus total widths Γ become very much greater than the spacing D, and the S_l are then slowly varying functions of momentum. As the energy increases, it is therefore to be expected that

$$\langle |S_l|^2 \rangle - |\langle S_l \rangle|^2 \to 0, \qquad (1.2\text{-}13)$$

so that

$$\sigma_{ce} \to 0$$
$$\sigma_c \to \sigma_r \qquad (1.2\text{-}14)$$
$$\sigma_{se} \to \sigma_s .$$

In the optical model, the averaged functions $\langle S_l \rangle$ are derived from the complex optical model potential. The total scattering

INTRODUCTION 9

cross section predicted by the optical model is therefore the shape elastic cross section, σ_{se}, and not the measured cross section $\langle\sigma_s\rangle$. Similarly, the model predicts the cross section for compound nucleus formation, σ_c, and not $\langle\sigma_r\rangle$, the averaged reaction cross section. Fortunately, however, the compound elastic scattering, which is the difference between the shape elastic and the measured energy-averaged scattering cross section, is believed not to be important, for nucleon scattering by medium or heavy nuclei, at nucleon energies greater than about 10 Mev. At lower energies, though, it should be considered. Compound elastic scattering is also responsible for difficulties in interpreting the differential cross section, which is given by

$$\frac{d\sigma_s}{d\Omega} = \frac{\pi}{k^2}\left|\sum_l (2l+1)^{1/2}(1-S_l)Y_{l,0}(\theta)\right|^2. \quad (1.2\text{-}15)$$

The differential cross section measured experimentally, in a scattering experiment with a beam of poor energy resolution, is the average of equation 1.2-15 and is not related in any simple way to the differential cross section obtained by making the replacement $S_l \to \langle S_l \rangle$. Thus,

$$\left\langle\frac{d\sigma_s}{d\Omega}\right\rangle = \frac{d\sigma_{se}}{d\Omega} + \frac{d\sigma_{ce}}{d\Omega}, \quad (1.2\text{-}16)$$

where the last term is the compound elastic differential cross section. There would appear to be no simple and rigorous method of estimating this. A discussion of compound elastic scattering and other limitations of the optical model is given in Sections 3.1 and 3.3. A further problem at low energies, and one which is most important for the light nuclei, is the choice of an interval I which is sufficient to include many levels of the compound nucleus.

The distinction between compound elastic and shape elastic scattering was made more clear by the time-dependent treatment of the problem presented by Friedman and Weisskopf (1955). They show that the scattering of a wave-packet comprising a broad spectrum of energies takes place in two stages.

The first is completed in a time of order $\hbar \, U^{-1} \approx 10^{-23}$ second and is the shape elastic scattering, the scattering caused by the optical model potential. This is also known as scattering by direct interaction. Formation of a compound nucleus is also possible. This may decay into a neutron and the original target nucleus in its ground state, a state of the whole system which is known as the entrance channel. This second stage, the compound elastic scattering, is completed in a time of order $\hbar \Gamma^{-1} \approx 10^{-15}$ second if $\Gamma \approx 1$ ev, which is long when measured on nuclear time scales. Provided the energy width of the incident wave-packet is very much greater than Γ, it is clear that experiments can be devised in which the scattered wave packets corresponding to the two stages cannot interfere. This is the origin of the simple additivity shown in equation 1.2–08. Charged particles can emit a photon before or after interacting with the target nucleus, and Eisberg, Yennie, and Wilkinson (1960) have shown that the time interval between formation and decay of the compound nucleus may be estimated, in principle, by precise measurement of this bremsstrahlung spectrum.

The success of the optical model in correlating the positions of the giant resonances and in describing the nucleon differential elastic scattering cross sections for a wide range of energies and target mass numbers, shows clearly that the model is valid. The radial extent of the potential is found to be consistent with, but not the same as the extent of the nuclear charge distribution determined by high energy electron scattering (the results of the electron scattering experiments have been summarised by Ravenhall, 1958). This, together with the fact that the depth of the real part of the potential is reasonable from the point of view of the shell model and has little variation with nucleon energy or target mass number, provides much support for the model. Measurements of the shape and strength and variations with energy and mass number of both real and imaginary parts of the potential are of great importance as they provide a method of investigating nuclear structure. An account of this is given in Sections 2.8 and 3.1–3.4.

At least as important, however, is the problem of why the model is successful. This differs from the problem of understanding the success of the shell model in that the excitation energies involved in the optical model are large, being usually greater than 8 Mev. For a very strong coupling of the incident nucleon to the target, the compound nucleus model would be expected to be good. That the coupling is not sufficiently strong is shown by the existence of the giant resonances, some understanding of which may be obtained from the intermediate model of Lane, Thomas, and Wigner (1955). A further, and more difficult, problem is the relation between the optical model potential and the nucleon-nucleon potentials. This particular problem, even if complete (numerical) solutions are not obtained, is of interest in that it can give information about general properties of the potential such as its shape and the form of the nonlocality. Such ideas form a useful adjunct to the phenomenological analysis described in Sections 3.2 and 3.3.

1.3 Measurement of Nuclear Size

It will be useful to note some basic facts concerning the scattering of a particle by a complex potential. For present purposes, it is sufficient to assume that the potential is local (see Section 2.1) and includes no terms representing spin-orbit coupling. An account of the spin-orbit coupling in the optical model is given in Sections 3.2 and 3.3.

The square well potential (equation 1.1-02) was found to give too great a differential cross section for large scattering angles (Woods and Saxon, 1954; Chase and Rohrlich, 1954). Woods and Saxon suggested a form having a diffuse edge and were able to show, for the scattering of 20 Mev protons, that such a potential gave a more satisfactory fit to the experimental differential cross section. Their potential is

$$V(r) = (U - iW) \left\{ 1 + \exp\left(\frac{r - R}{a}\right) \right\}^{-1}, \quad (1.3\text{-}01)$$

it being approximately true that R measures the radial extent of the potential and a its diffuseness. The value of U (it is of the order of -50 Mev), and the radial extent, make it clear that approximate methods[1] of calculating the parameters S_l are not likely to be sufficiently accurate for incident nucleons of low or intermediate energy. However, exact numerical solutions of the Schrödinger equation may be obtained with modern electronic digital computers. The Schrödinger equation is

$$\nabla^2 \psi(\mathbf{r}) + 2M\{E - V(r)\}\psi(\mathbf{r}) = 0, \qquad (1.3\text{-}02)$$

where E is the centre of mass energy and M the reduced mass of the incident particle. The whole system has axial symmetry about the direction of the incident particle, and the expansion into partial wave functions

$$\psi(\mathbf{r}) = \frac{1}{kr} \sum_l \phi_l(kr) Y_{l,0}(\theta) \qquad (1.3\text{-}03)$$

may be carried out, where

$$k^2 = 2\,ME, \qquad (1.3\text{-}04)$$

and θ is measured from the direction of the incident particle. The partial wave functions ϕ_l satisfy

$$\frac{d^2\phi_l}{dr^2} + 2M(E - V)\phi_l - \frac{l(l+1)}{r^2}\,\phi_l = 0. \quad (1.3\text{-}05)$$

The sign of the imaginary part of the potential (1.3-01) is a matter of convention. The one adopted, $W > 0$, gives the result

$$|S_l| \leqslant 1,$$

and is consistent with the factor e^{ikr} representing an outgoing wave. Reaction cross sections for individual partial waves (equation 1.2-03) are then always positive. By writing down the complex conjugate of equation 1.3-05, it is easy to see that the change $W \to -W$ results in $\phi_l \to \phi_l^*$.

The Born approximation provides a useful indication of the

[1] See, for example, Mott and Massey (1949), or Landau and Lifshitz (1958).

most important features of the scattering by a complex potential.
The Born approximation scattering amplitude is

$$f_B = -\frac{M}{2\pi} \int d\mathbf{r} \; V(r) e^{-i(\mathbf{k}_2 - \mathbf{k}_1) \cdot \mathbf{r}}, \qquad (1.3\text{-}06)$$

where $\mathbf{k}_1$ and $\mathbf{k}_2$ are the initial and final centre of mass momenta.
The momentum transfer in the collision is therefore $\mathbf{q} = \mathbf{k}_2 - \mathbf{k}_1$, and in this approximation, provided V is a function of r, f_B depends on q only and is independent of the energy. f_B is therefore proportional to the three-dimensional Fourier transform of the potential. After the integrations over the angular variables have been performed,

$$f_B = -\frac{2M}{q} \int_0^\infty r \sin qr \; V(r) dr. \qquad (1.3\text{-}07)$$

Expanding the term $\sin qr$ in powers of (qr),

$$f_B = -\frac{M}{2\pi} \left\{ V^{(0)} - \frac{q^2}{3!} V^{(2)} + \frac{q^4}{5!} V^{(4)} - \cdots \right\}, \qquad (1.3\text{-}08)$$

where $V^{(n)}$ is the nth moment[2] of the potential,

$$V^{(n)} = \int d\mathbf{r} \; r^n V(r). \qquad (1.3\text{-}09)$$

The momentum transfer and the scattering angle, θ, in the centre of mass system are connected by

$$q = 2k \sin \frac{\theta}{2}, \qquad (1.3\text{-}10)$$

and the differential cross section is

$$\frac{d\sigma}{d\Omega} = |f_B|^2. \qquad (1.3\text{-}11)$$

From equation 1.3-08 it is clear that the differential cross section for scattering through small angles determines $V^{(0)}$ and the

---

[2] It is assumed here that the potential $V(r)$ is of short range so that the moments exist. This is not true for the Coulomb potential.

second moment $V^{(2)}$, which measures the radial extent of the potential. Further information about the shape of the potential, such as a determination of the diffuseness parameter a, requires measurement of higher moments which depend on the differential cross section at larger angles. From 1.3-06 and 1.3-10, the angular width of the forward peak in the differential cross section decreases as either the radial extent of the potential or the momentum, k, of the incident particle increase. These general properties are correct for the exact scattering amplitude, and form a basis for the measurement of nuclear size by the elastic scattering of nucleons.

To describe the scattering of charged particles, in the Born approximation, a Coulomb amplitude should be added to f_B. The Coulomb amplitude is,[3]

$$f_C = -\frac{\beta}{2k} \operatorname{cosec}^2 \frac{\theta}{2} \, e^{i\left(2\sigma_0 - \beta \ln\left(\sin^2 \frac{\theta}{2}\right)\right)} , \qquad (1.3\text{-}12)$$

where

$$\beta = \frac{ZZ'e^2M}{k} , \qquad (1.3\text{-}13)$$

Z and Z' being the charges of the target nucleus and incident particle respectively. The $l = 0$ Coulomb phase shift σ_0 is the argument of a gamma function,[3] thus,

$$\sigma_0 = \arg \Gamma(1 + i\beta). \qquad (1.3\text{-}14)$$

To investigate the interference between the amplitudes f_B and f_c it is sufficient to represent them by the complex numbers Xe^{ix} and Ye^{iy}, respectively. Then changing the sign of the charge of the incident particle causes

$$\left.\begin{array}{r} \beta \to -\beta \\ Y \to -Y \\ y \to -y \end{array}\right\} \qquad (1.3\text{-}15)$$

[3] Landau and Lifshitz (1958), p. 419.

From 1.3-11, the differential cross section is

$$| X |^2 + | Y |^2 + 2 XY \cos (x - y), \qquad (1.3\text{-}16)$$

and if the sign of the charge of the incident particle is changed, it is

$$| X |^2 + | Y |^2 - 2 XY \cos (x + y). \qquad (1.3\text{-}17)$$

The difference between these two differential cross sections is

$$2 XY \{\cos (x - y) + \cos (x + y)\} = 4 XY \cos x \cos y. \qquad (1.3\text{-}18)$$

This quantity is a measure of the Coulomb interference which is therefore greatest when $x = 0$, corresponding, in the Born approximation, to a real optical model potential. A purely imaginary potential, $\cos x = 0$, gives, in this approximation, no interference. Another way of looking at the problem is to write down the change in the differential cross section which results if the sign of the real part of the potential is changed. The cross section 1.3-16 is replaced by

$$| X |^2 + | Y |^2 + 2 XY \cos (\pi - x - y). \qquad (1.3\text{-}19)$$

The difference between 1.3-16 and 1.3-19 is given by equation 1.3-18, and the previous comments still apply.

The imaginary part of the optical model potential therefore has the property of damping out Coulomb interference effects.

As a function of momentum transfer, the differential cross section for a charged particle has the following properties: for small q, $| Y | \gg | X |$, as $| Y |$ is proportional to $1/q^2$, and the differential cross section is well described by Rutherford's scattering formula; $| Y | \approx | X |$ defines the region in which interference is most important; for large q, $| Y | \ll | X |$ and the differential cross section depends on the optical model potential. Once again, these general properties are correct for the exact scattering amplitude. The Coulomb interference region is of interest in the elastic scattering of mesons by nuclei. An experimental determination of the sign of the interference term in the differential cross section 1.3-16 is possible so that the sign of cos x can be found. A more complete account of this subject is given in Section 3.5.

1.4 Numerical Solution of the Wave Equation

The most simple wave equation is the Schrödinger equation in which both incident particle and target nucleus are assumed to have spin 0. This is sufficient to demonstrate the method of solution. If the incident particle has a spin of $\frac{1}{2}$, and spin-orbit coupling terms are included in the potential, as is now usual, some modifications to the formalism presented here are required. For further details, we refer to the paper of Buck, Maddison, and Hodgson (1960).

The starting point is equation 1.3-05, for charged particles V having the asymptotic form $ZZ'e^2/r$ for values of r outside the nuclear volume. The asymptotic solution, $\phi_l(kr)$, with the correct boundary conditions is

$$\sqrt{\pi}\sqrt{2l+1}\ (i)^{l+1}\{e^{-i\alpha} - S_l e^{i\alpha}\} \qquad (1.4\text{-}01)$$

as $r \to \infty$, where

$$\alpha = kr - \tfrac{1}{2}\,l\pi - \beta \ln (2\,kr), \qquad (1.4\text{-}02)$$

and β is defined by equation 1.3-13. The extra terms containing $\beta \ln (2\,kr)$, by which 1.4-01 differs from 1.2-01, are a consequence of the long range of the Coulomb potential. The parameter S_l is related to the complete phase shift, which includes the effect of both the coulomb and the optical model potentials, by $S_l = \exp(2i\delta_l)$. For Coulomb scattering by a point charge, $S_l = \exp(2\,i\sigma_l)$, where σ_l is the Coulomb phase shift, defined by

$$\sigma_l = \arg \Gamma(1 + l + i\beta). \qquad (1.4\text{-}03)$$

The Coulomb phase shifts for higher values of l may be calculated in terms of σ_0 by the relation, for gamma functions,

$$\Gamma(z + 1) = z\Gamma(z). \qquad (1.4\text{-}04)$$

Other methods are described in the paper of Buck, Maddison, and Hodgson (1960). The solution (1.4-01) is constructed from the regular and irregular Coulomb functions, F_l and G_l, which are the two linearly independent solutions of equation 1.3-05 for V equal to the Coulomb potential only. They have the asymptotic forms

$$F_l(kr) \sim \sin (\alpha + \sigma_l) \qquad (1.4\text{-}05)$$

and

$$G_l(kr) \sim \cos (\alpha + \sigma_l) \qquad (1.4\text{-}06)$$

as $r \to \infty$. The ingoing wave part of 1.4-01 is

$$e^{-i\alpha} = e^{i\sigma_l}(G_l - iF_l), \qquad (1.4\text{-}07)$$

and the outgoing part,

$$e^{i\alpha} = e^{-i\sigma_l}(G_l + iF_l). \qquad (1.4\text{-}08)$$

A critical survey of methods of calculating F_l and G_l for values of r of the order of the nuclear radius, and also σ_l, has been given by Buck, Maddison, and Hodgson (1960). Given these functions, the solution of 1.3-05 as a function of r may be continued in from infinity where the solution is 1.4-01 to a point $r = r_m$, r_m usually lying between $2R$ and $5R$. In this solution, $\phi_l(kr)$, in the outer region $r \geqslant r_m$, S_l appears explicitly as a free parameter. Numerical integration of 1.3-05 in the region $r \leqslant r_m$, including both the optical model and Coulomb potentials, is then carried out starting from the boundary condition at the origin $\phi_l(0) = 0$, which is necessary if the wave function $\psi(\mathbf{r})$ is to be finite. Let this interior solution be $\phi_l^{(i)}(kr)$. From the requirement that the wave function and its first derivative be continuous for all r,

$$\left\{ \frac{1}{\phi_l^{(i)}} \frac{d\phi_l^{(i)}}{dr} \right\}_{r=r_m} = \left\{ \frac{1}{\phi_l} \frac{d\phi_l}{dr} \right\}_{r=r_m} \qquad (1.4\text{-}09)$$

As the functions ϕ_l are complex, equation 1.4-09 implies two conditions, this being the number necessary to determine the real and imaginary parts of S_l.

The exact scattering amplitude is then

$$f(\theta) = f_c + \frac{1}{2ik} \sum_{l=0}^{l_m} (2l + 1)(S_l - e^{2i\sigma_l})P_l\,(\cos\theta), \quad (1.4\text{-}10)$$

where l_m is the maximum value of the angular momentum and f_C is defined by 1.3-12. The amplitude

$$f_C - \frac{1}{2ik} \sum_{l=0}^{l_m} (2l + 1)(e^{2i\sigma_l} - 1)P_l\,(\cos\theta) \quad (1.4\text{-}11)$$

is the sum of all the partial wave amplitudes for $l > l_m$ and is purely Coulomb in origin. The differential cross section is $|f(\theta)|^2$ and the reaction cross section is

$$\sigma_r = \frac{\pi}{k^2} \sum_{l=0}^{l_m} (2l + 1)(1 - |S_l|^2). \quad (1.4\text{-}12)$$

The value of l_m depends on the energy of the particle and on the mass number of the target nucleus. A sufficient value is usually given, very roughly, by $l_m = 2\,kR$, R being the Saxon-Woods parameter appearing in 1.3-01. The sufficiency though, requires to be checked for each calculation.

The equation appropriate to relativistic spin 0 particles is the Klein-Gordon equation. Though not strictly a wave equation,[4] it gives a satisfactory description of the current of spin 0 particles, enabling the cross sections to be defined.

The Hamiltonian, including the electromagnetic interaction only and neglecting target recoil, is

$$H = V_C + \{(\mathbf{k} - Z'e\mathbf{A})^2 + M^2\}^{1/2} \quad (1.4\text{-}13)$$

where $\mathbf{A}$ is the vector potential and V_C the Coulomb potential. The optical model potential, if it has simple properties under a proper Lorentz transformation, could transform either as a scalar or a four-vector. For the vector possibility, it would be natural to identify the potential described in earlier sections with the fourth component. However, there is no information about the other three components (analogous to $\mathbf{A}$), and there is at most one frame of reference in which these could all vanish.

[4] Schweber, Bethe, and de Hoffmann (1955), pp. 4–8.

It is usual to assume that this is the laboratory system. If the nucleus is heavy, and therefore moving slowly after the collision, it is reasonable to neglect the electromagnetic interaction involving **A**. With these assumptions, the Hamiltonian is

$$H = V_C + V(r) + (\mathbf{k}^2 + M^2)^{1/2}, \qquad (1.4\text{-}14)$$

and the Klein-Gordon equation is

$$\nabla^2\psi(\mathbf{r}) + (E - V_c - V)^2\psi(\mathbf{r}) - M^2\psi(\mathbf{r}) = 0, \quad (1.4\text{-}15)$$

where E is here the total energy, including rest mass. If the optical model potential were a scalar, the Hamiltonian would be

$$H = V_C + \{\mathbf{k}^2 + (M + V)^2\}^{1/2} \qquad (1.4\text{-}16)$$

leading to the Klein-Gordon equation

$$\nabla^2\psi(\mathbf{r}) + (E - V_C)^2\psi(\mathbf{r}) - (M + V)^2\psi(\mathbf{r}) = 0. \quad (1.4\text{-}17)$$

Both equations 1.4-15 and 1.4-17 have the same nonrelativistic limit, which is obtained by letting M tend to infinity. The expansion into partial wave functions may be carried out, as for the Schrödinger equation, by equation 1.3-03. The only new feature which appears in the equations (analogous to 1.3-05) for the partial wave functions is that terms which are quadratic in the potentials are present. The solutions of these equations may be obtained by the method outlined in the earlier part of this section. However, the Coulomb functions F_l and G_l, although having the same asymptotic form, will for general values of r be different from the non-relativistic functions owing to the terms quadratic in the Coulomb potential. The two equations 1.4-15 and 1.4-17 lead to different partial wave equations and therefore, for a given potential V, to different cross sections.

CHAPTER 2

Justification of the Model

Sections 2.2 and 2.3 contain an account of derivations of the optical model starting from an expansion of the scattering amplitude in powers of the strength of the nucleon-nucleon potential. The problem of the hard core in the nucleon-nucleon potential can be solved by summation of certain parts of the perturbation series, and this method is outlined in Section 2.2.

The Green's function 2.2-05 which appears in the expansion is such that the incident nucleon and the target propagate as free systems. An alternative Green's function is given by 2.2-13, which describes the propagation of the incident nucleon in a dispersive medium, and applications of this have been given by Watson (1957).

A simple expansion in powers of the strength of the nucleon-nucleon potential is not useful in energy regions where the states of the compound nucleus have small widths, and Sections 2.4 2.5, and 2.6 therefore give an account of the derivation of the optical model starting from the dispersion formulae for nuclear and potential scattering. A unified formalism has been presented by Bloch (1957), which can be used to derive the expansion in powers of the strength of the nucleon-nucleon potential, the Kapur-Peierls formalism, and the Wigner-Eisenbud formalism.

The identity of the incident and target nucleons is not taken into account in this chapter because the most important results of the optical model do not depend on it. The identity is taken into account in Appendix B, which gives a derivation of the single-particle or optical model potential for an infinite target.

It is shown that the exchange correction is not important for incident nucleons of high energy. The theory contained in Appendix B can be applied to finite target nuclei (Shaw, 1959) if the Thomas-Fermi approximation is made.

In this chapter, a single-particle width is denoted by Γ, and a many-particle width by γ.

2.1 Some Results in the Theory of Scattering

The optical model is known to be successful in describing the elastic scattering and reaction cross sections for high energy particles. The problem of understanding why the potential has the simple properties which are found may be solved by constructing a theory which relates the potential to the particle-nucleon interaction and the known properties of the target nucleus. Such a theory, involving many particles, is most conveniently set out in terms of the abstract vector formulation of quantum mechanics devised by Dirac (1947). We shall now give a summary of the results which will be required in later sections. This will, in addition, establish the notation used and serve to define the nonlocal potential which invariably appears when a many-body problem is reduced to an equivalent single-particle problem. Complete derivations will not be given.

We shall require the completeness conditions for the states of a single free particle. These are (Dirac, 1947, p. 63),

$$\frac{1}{(2\pi)^3} \int d\mathbf{k} \mid \mathbf{k} \rangle \langle \mathbf{k} \mid = 1, \qquad (2.1\text{-}01)$$

and

$$\int d\mathbf{r} \mid \mathbf{r} \rangle \langle \mathbf{r} \mid = 1, \qquad (2.1\text{-}02)$$

where the right-hand side in both equations stands for the unit operator.

The matrix element of an interaction connecting two states, for example, of a single free particle, is denoted by

$$\langle \mathbf{k}' \mid V \mid \mathbf{k} \rangle. \qquad (2.1\text{-}03)$$

It is useful to transform the matrix element by using the unit operator 2.1-02. There are two places in 2.1-03 where the unit operator may be introduced, and the two resulting integrations are independent. Therefore, 2.1-03 is transformed to

$$\iint d\mathbf{r}' \, d\mathbf{r} \, e^{-i\mathbf{k}'\cdot\mathbf{r}'} V(\mathbf{r}', \mathbf{r}) \, e^{i\mathbf{k}\cdot\mathbf{r}} \qquad (2.1\text{-}04)$$

(Dirac, p. 80), where the interaction V is represented as a function of the space coordinate. This function may be defined as the interaction potential. It is known as a nonlocal potential because it depends on the coordinate of the particle in two independent ways. The two dependences are equivalent, that is

$$V(\mathbf{r}', \mathbf{r}) = V(\mathbf{r}, \mathbf{r}') \qquad (2.1\text{-}05)$$

(Brown and De Dominicis, 1958).

A local potential is defined by the equation

$$V(\mathbf{r}', \mathbf{r}) = V(r)\delta(\mathbf{r}' - \mathbf{r}) \qquad (2.1\text{-}06)$$

and is a special case of the more general nonlocal potential. There is evidence that the optical model potential is nonlocal, and therefore a further discussion of this subject will be given in Section 2.8. It is sufficient, for the moment, to stress that as far as strong interactions are concerned, the concept of a local potential is an idealization.

We now give some identities which will be useful. It will be necessary to represent a function of a hermitian operator in terms of the eigenvalues and eigenstates of the operator. Let us consider the energy operator (or Hamiltonian) of a single free particle. The eigenvalues and eigenstates are given by the set of equations

$$K \mid \mathbf{k} \rangle = e(k) \mid \mathbf{k} \rangle. \qquad (2.1\text{-}07)$$

The function of K we require is $(E - K)^{-1}$ for complex values of E. Since the eigenstates of a hermitian operator form a complete orthogonal set, the representation is

$$\frac{1}{E - K} = \frac{1}{(2\pi)^3} \int d\mathbf{k} \, \frac{| \, \mathbf{k} \rangle \, \langle \mathbf{k} \, |}{E - e(k)} \qquad (2.1\text{-}08)$$

$$(\text{complex } E)$$

(equation 2.1-01 and Dirac, p. 41). For real values of E, this formula is without meaning because the denominator $E - e(k)$ can vanish. The representation is only valid when E lies in the complex plane and the denominator therefore never becomes zero. The problem of evaluating such quantities in the limit when E tends to the real axis leads to the next identity.

Consider a definite integral of the form

$$\int_{C_1} \frac{f(z') \, dz'}{z' - x} \qquad (2.1\text{-}09)$$

in which x and z' are real and complex variables respectively. The function $f(z')$ is analytic on and near the real axis, which is a sufficient condition for the validity of the identity to be given. The contour C_1 is parallel to the real axis but displaced from it by an amount $+i\epsilon$, where ϵ is an infinitesimal positive number. In the limit $\epsilon \rightarrow +0$,

$$\int_{C_1} \frac{f(z') \, dz'}{z' - x} = \int_{C_2} \frac{f(z') \, dz'}{z' - x} - 2\pi i f(x) \qquad (2.1\text{-}10)$$

where C_2 is of the same length as C_1 but is displaced from the real axis by $-i\epsilon$. The sum of the integrals over the contours C_1 and C_2 is twice the principal value of the integral, and therefore

$$\int_{C_1} \frac{f(z') \, dz'}{z' - x} = P \int \frac{f(x') \, dx'}{x' - x} - i\pi f(x). \qquad (2.1\text{-}11)$$

These results may be summarised by the formal identity

$$\lim_{\epsilon \rightarrow +0} \frac{1}{x' - x \pm i\epsilon} = P \, \frac{1}{x' - x} \mp i\pi\delta(x' - x). \qquad (2.1\text{-}12)$$

It is now possible to summarise some scattering formulae. The interaction V, when represented by a potential, is taken to be of short range and is fixed at the origin of coordinates. When V is not present, the eigenstate associated with energy E satisfies

$$K \mid \mathbf{k} \rangle = E \mid \mathbf{k} \rangle \qquad (2.1\text{-}13)$$

where K is the kinetic energy operator and $k^2 = 2ME$. With V included,

$$H = K + V, \qquad H \mid \psi \rangle = E \mid \psi \rangle \qquad (2.1\text{-}14)$$

The problem is to determine $\mid \psi \rangle$. There is no shift in energy unless the system is enclosed in a potential box of finite size. For a complex energy, denoted by $E + i\epsilon$, we can construct

$$\frac{1}{E - K + i\epsilon} \qquad (2.1\text{-}15)$$

which is a well-behaved operator. From 2.1-13, 2.1-14, and 2.1-15, it follows that

$$\mid \psi \rangle = \mid \mathbf{k} \rangle + \frac{1}{E - K + i\epsilon} \, V \mid \psi \rangle + O(\epsilon) \quad (2.1\text{-}16)$$

where $O(\epsilon)$ denotes a contribution to the state $\mid \psi \rangle$ which vanishes in the limit $\mid \epsilon \mid \to 0$.

The exact amplitude for a transition from a state of centre of mass momentum $\mathbf{k}$ to one of $\mathbf{k}'$ is given by the matrix element of the T-operator, which is defined by

$$\langle \mathbf{k}' \mid T \mid \mathbf{k} \rangle = \langle \mathbf{k}' \mid V \mid \psi \rangle. \qquad (2.1\text{-}17)$$

Equations 2.1-16 and 2.1-17 therefore lead to the operator equation

$$T = \lim_{\mid \epsilon \mid \to 0} \left\{ V + V \, \frac{1}{E - K + i\epsilon} \, T \right\}. \qquad (2.1\text{-}18)$$

The sign of ϵ is connected with the possible boundary conditions, and for a complete discussion we refer to any of the review papers quoted at the end of this section. Let ϵ be positive.

Then by equations 2.1-02 and 2.1-08, and a simple contour integration, we have for the wave function corresponding to the state $|\psi\rangle$,

$$\psi(\mathbf{r}) = e^{i\mathbf{k}\cdot\mathbf{r}} - \frac{M}{2\pi} \iint d\mathbf{r}' \, d\mathbf{r}'' \, \frac{e^{ik|\mathbf{r}-\mathbf{r}'|}}{|\mathbf{r}-\mathbf{r}'|} \, V(\mathbf{r}', \mathbf{r}'')\psi(\mathbf{r}''),$$

(2.1-19)

for $\epsilon \to +0$. For large values of r, the wave function is

$$\psi(\mathbf{r}) \sim e^{i\mathbf{k}\cdot\mathbf{r}} + \frac{f e^{ikr}}{r},$$ (2.1-20)

where the scattering amplitude is

$$f = -\frac{M}{2\pi} \langle \mathbf{k}' \mid T \mid \mathbf{k} \rangle.$$ (2.1-21)

This result is nonrelativistic because in order to derive equation 2.1-19 we have assumed the kinetic energy of the particle in both real and virtual states to be small compared with its rest mass. Equation 2.1-16 is equivalent to the Born integral equation for the scattering wave function (Mott and Massey, 1949, p. 116). This integral equation is equivalent to the Schrödinger equation but, in addition, contains the boundary conditions necessary for a scattering state. The inclusion, and correct choice of boundary conditions, is made possible by the complex energy $E + i\epsilon$. The limit $\epsilon \to +0$ corresponds to the boundary condition in which the scattered waves are outgoing. The limit $\epsilon \to -0$ would give scattered waves depending asymptotically on e^{-ikr}, in disagreement with the convention adopted in Section 1.3

The perturbation series obtained by iteration of 2.1-18,

$$T = \lim_{\epsilon \to +0} \left\{ V + V \frac{1}{E - K + i\epsilon} V \right.$$

$$\left. + V \frac{1}{E - K + i\epsilon} V \frac{1}{E - K + i\epsilon} V + \cdots \right\},$$

(2.1-22)

is the Born series for the transition amplitude. From 2.1-21 and 2.1-22, the first Born approximation to the scattering amplitude is

$$-\frac{M}{2\pi} \langle \mathbf{k}' \mid V \mid \mathbf{k} \rangle, \tag{2.1-23}$$

which is identical with equation 1.3-06.

The series 2.1-22 is not always convergent. For example, it is not convergent near zero energy in the case of the nucleon-nucleon isotopic spin 0, spin $J = 1$, and even parity state. For these quantum numbers there is one bound state, the deuteron, and a theorem given by Levinson (1949) shows that as the energy tends to zero, the phase shift tends to the value π. The $l = 0$ scattering amplitude

$$f = \frac{1}{2ik} (S_0 - 1) \tag{2.1-24}$$

is therefore negative in sign near zero energy, so that by 2.1-21, the transition amplitude must be positive. However, the real part of each term[1] in the Born series 2.1-22 is negative in sign (the imaginary parts tend to zero as E tends to zero). Therefore, the sum of the terms in the series is not equal to the value of the transition amplitude, and we can see that the series is not uniformly convergent as E tends to zero. Further examples of series which are not uniformly convergent in some specified region will occur in Section 2.3.

The integral equations are still valid in this case but may not be solved by direct iteration. For local static potentials, bounded and of finite range, the problem of finding sufficient conditions for convergence of the Born series has been successfully considered by Davies (1960), who also gives references to earlier work. The series for the scattering amplitude is convergent at all positive energies if $- \mid V(r) \mid$ has no bound states.

[1] The potential is taken to be a smooth function of r, for example, the Yukawa form. If the potential has a hard core the terms in 2.1-22 are all infinite.

It is not intended that the account of scattering theory presented in this section should be regarded as complete. Gell-Mann and Goldberger (1953) have derived 2.1-18 from a time-dependent theory of scattering. Further complete descriptions of the theory are those of Møller (1945), Dirac (1947), and Lippmann and Schwinger (1950).

2.2 The High Energy Expansion for the Optical Model Operator

In this section we shall describe the scattering of a particle by a nucleus regarded as a system of A nucleons. For this problem, the definition of the optical model operator is found to lead to some simplification.[2] The optical model potential is that function of the space coordinate of the incident particle which represents the optical model operator. Some discussion of the potential will be given in the next section, but for the present, we shall be concerned with the operator only. A connection will be established between the optical model operator, $\mathbf{U}$, and the interactions between the incident particle and separate nucleons in the target nucleus. The main results of this section are contained in equations 2.2-15, 2.2-33, 2.2-38, 2.2-40, and 2.2-41.

It is assumed, for the moment, that the incident particle is not a compound particle and is not capable of producing different particles by interaction with a nucleon.

Let H_1 be the Hamiltonian of the nucleus, and E_1 the energy eigenvalue. The equation of motion for the nucleus is

$$H_1 \mid \mu \rangle = E_1(\mu) \mid \mu \rangle. \qquad (2.2\text{-}01)$$

H_1 is assumed to be hermitian so that the states $\mid \mu \rangle$ form a complete orthogonal set with ground state $\mid \mu_0 \rangle$. The equation of motion for the incident particle, when there is no interaction with the nucleus, is

$$H_2 \mid \mathbf{k}' \rangle = E_2(k') \mid \mathbf{k}' \rangle, \qquad (2.2\text{-}02)$$

[2] The basic principles described in this section are contained in a number of papers by Watson and collaborators. Both a summary and a list of references are given in the papers by Watson (1957 and 1958).

where $\mathbf{k}'$ is the momentum.   If the incident particle is a nucleon, it should, in principle, be antisymmetrized with the A nucleons in the nucleus.   This is not essential for the derivation of the main results of this section, which are most useful when the incident particle is of high energy.   The error in the optical model operator resulting from failure to antisymmetrize an incident nucleon of, for example, 100 Mev, with the relatively slow nucleons bound in the nucleus is not expected to be important.   Some further discussion of the problems of antisymmetrization is given at the end of the section.

The direct product of the two complete and orthogonal sets defined by 2.2-01 and 2.2-02 is itself complete and orthogonal and forms a useful basic set of states for the whole system. These product states are denoted by $|\,\mu,\,\mathbf{k}'\rangle$.   The total energy is the sum of the energies of the two independent systems, that is

$$E = E_1(\mu_0) + E_2(k). \qquad (2.2\text{-}03)$$

If V is the interaction between the incident particle and the nucleus, the equivalent for the many-particle system of equation 2.1-16 is

$$|\Psi\rangle = |\,\mu_0,\,\mathbf{k}\rangle + G(E)V\,|\Psi\rangle \qquad (2.2\text{-}04)$$

where

$$G(E) = (E - H_1 - H_2 + i\epsilon)^{-1}, \qquad (2.2\text{-}05)$$

and ϵ is infinitesimal and positive.   Equation 2.2-04 differs from the equation 2.1-16 for two particles only, in that $|\Psi\rangle$ contains components which do not correspond to elastic scattering. This may be seen by writing down the series solution of 2.2-04 obtained by iteration.   The series is

$$|\Psi\rangle = (1 + GV + GVGV + \cdots)\,|\,\mu_0,\,\mathbf{k}\rangle. \qquad (2.2\text{-}06)$$

The interaction V, operating on $|\,\mu_0,\,\mathbf{k}\rangle$, is capable of changing the state of the target so that $|\Psi\rangle$ will contain states $|\,\mu,\,\mathbf{k}'\rangle$ for $\mu \neq \mu_0$, which describe inelastic scattering.   The elastic scattering components of $|\Psi\rangle$ must therefore be separated.   Since the basic vectors are orthogonal, the state vector for elastic scattering is

$$| \Phi \rangle = \frac{1}{(2\pi)^3} \int d\mathbf{k}' \, | \mu_0, \mathbf{k}' \rangle \langle \mu_0, \mathbf{k}' | \Psi \rangle. \quad (2.2\text{-}07)$$

The optical model operator is the interaction which leads to the elastic scattering state vector $| \Phi \rangle$ and is therefore defined by the equation

$$| \Phi \rangle = | \mu_0, \mathbf{k} \rangle + G(E)\mathbf{U} | \Phi \rangle. \quad (2.2\text{-}08)$$

The most important property of $\mathbf{U}$ may be obtained from the definition 2.2-07. This means that

$$\langle \mu, \mathbf{k}' | \Phi \rangle = 0, \quad (2.2\text{-}09)$$

for all $\mu \neq \mu_0$. From 2.2-08, the operator $\mathbf{U}$ must be such that acting on $| \mu_0, \mathbf{k} \rangle$ in which the target is in the ground state, it produces only components $| \mu_0, \mathbf{k}' \rangle$. It cannot change the state of the target. Therefore, it is possible to write

$$\langle \mu, \mathbf{k}' | \mathbf{U} | \mu_0, \mathbf{k} \rangle = \delta_{\mu\mu_0} \langle \mathbf{k}' | \mathbf{U} | \mathbf{k} \rangle, \quad (2.2\text{-}10)$$

and $\mathbf{U}$ is referred to as a single-particle operator. The problem is now to obtain a connection between $\mathbf{U}$ and V.

Let us introduce the operator $\mathfrak{F}$ (Watson, 1957) such that

$$| \Psi \rangle = \mathfrak{F} | \Phi \rangle. \quad (2.2\text{-}11)$$

From 2.2-04 and 2.2-08, $\mathfrak{F}$ satisfies

$$\mathfrak{F} = 1 + \mathfrak{G}(E)(V - \mathbf{U})\mathfrak{F}, \quad (2.2\text{-}12)$$

where

$$\mathfrak{G}(E) = (E - H_1 - H_2 - \mathbf{U} + i\epsilon)^{-1}. \quad (2.2\text{-}13)$$

Equating the exact elastic transition amplitudes, associated with 2.2-04 and 2.2-08, to a final state $| \mu_0, \mathbf{k}' \rangle$, we have

$$\langle \mu_0, \mathbf{k}' | \mathbf{U} | \Phi \rangle = \langle \mu_0, \mathbf{k}' | V | \Psi \rangle$$
$$= \langle \mu_0, \mathbf{k}' | V\mathfrak{F} | \Phi \rangle. \quad (2.2\text{-}14)$$

From 2.2-12 and 2.2-14, we have the series

$$\langle \mathbf{U} \rangle = \langle V + V\mathfrak{G}(V - \mathbf{U}) + V\mathfrak{G}(V - \mathbf{U})\mathfrak{G}(V - \mathbf{U}) + \cdots \rangle,$$

$$(2.2\text{-}15)$$

where from now on the brackets mean that both sides of the equation appear in matrix elements of the form 2.2-14.

The next stage consists of the replacement of $\mathfrak{G}(E)$ by $G(E)$. In order to be able to do this, some further results are required. For any operators P and Q, which are nonsingular,

$$\frac{1}{P + Q} = \frac{1}{P} - \frac{1}{P} Q \frac{1}{P} + \cdots \qquad (2.2\text{-}16)$$

This result is analogous to the Neumann series in the theory of matrices (Courant and Hilbert, 1953, p. 9) and is useful in establishing connections between $\mathfrak{G}$ and G. From the definitions 2.2-05 and 2.2-13,

$$G(E) = \{\mathfrak{G}^{-1}(E) + \mathbf{U}\}^{-1} \qquad (2.2\text{-}17)$$

and applying 2.2-16, this becomes

$$G(E) = \mathfrak{G} - \mathfrak{G}\mathbf{U}\mathfrak{G} + \mathfrak{G}\mathbf{U}\mathfrak{G}\mathbf{U}\mathfrak{G} - \cdots \qquad (2.2\text{-}18)$$

A further result is

$$1 - G\mathbf{U} = 1 - \mathfrak{G}\mathbf{U} + \mathfrak{G}\mathbf{U}\mathfrak{G}\mathbf{U} - \cdots. \qquad (2.2\text{-}19)$$

Returning to 2.2-15, let us rearrange the series and consider the sum of all terms in which V appears a given number of times. This is the product

$$V(\mathfrak{G} - \mathfrak{G}\mathbf{U}\mathfrak{G} + \cdots)V \cdots$$

$$(\mathfrak{G} - \mathfrak{G}\mathbf{U}\mathfrak{G} + \cdots)V(1 - \mathfrak{G}\mathbf{U} + \cdots). \qquad (2.2\text{-}20)$$

The connections established by equations 2.2-18 and 2.2-19 can now be used to eliminate the series containing $\mathfrak{G}$, and 2.2-20 becomes

$$VGV \cdots VGV(1 - G\mathbf{U}). \qquad (2.2\text{-}21)$$

Equation 2.2-15 may therefore be replaced by

$$\langle \mathbf{U} \rangle = \langle (V + VGV + \cdots)(1 - G\mathbf{U}) \rangle. \qquad (2.2\text{-}22)$$

At the present stage, we have not assumed that V has any specific form. We now assume that V is the sum of all the two-body interactions between the incident particle and the nucleons in the target, that is

$$V = \sum_{i=1}^{A} v_i. \qquad (2.2\text{-}23)$$

Potential functions which depend on the coordinates of the incident particle and of two or more nucleons must certainly exist in the correct total Hamiltonian for the complete system, but at present there seems to be no evidence that they are important in nuclear physics.

The intermediate states which may occur in the scattering process are such that either the incident particle or the target, or both, may be in excited states. We find it convenient to separate the states in which only the incident particle is excited, the target remaining in the ground state, from all other possible intermediate states. The separation is made by defining the projection operators

$$\alpha = 1 - \frac{1}{(2\pi)^3} \int d\mathbf{k}' \, | \, \mu_0 , \mathbf{k}' \rangle \, \langle \mu_0 , \mathbf{k}' \, | \qquad (2.2\text{-}24)$$

and

$$\beta = 1 - \alpha. \qquad (2.2\text{-}25)$$

The operator β therefore projects out the target ground state. Iteration of 2.2-22 results in

$$\langle \mathbf{U} \rangle = \langle K - K\beta GK + K\beta GK\beta GK - \cdots \rangle, \qquad (2.2\text{-}26)$$

where

$$K = V + VGV + \cdots . \qquad (2.2\text{-}27)$$

If we insert the projection operators 2.2-24 and 2.2-25, the term in 2.2-27 having N operators V is the sum of 2^{N-1} different terms of the form

$$(V\alpha GV)\beta G(V)\beta G \cdots (V). \qquad (2.2\text{-}28)$$

The sum for all N of these products may be arranged according to the number of operators βG which appear in each product. Therefore, 2.2-27 may be rearranged in the form

$$K = L + L\beta GL + L\beta GL\beta GL + \cdots, \qquad (2.2\text{-}29)$$

where

$$L = V + V\alpha GV + \cdots. \qquad (2.2\text{-}30)$$

Application of the identity 2.1-08 to terms in the series 2.2-30 shows that the intermediate states are all such that the target and the incident particle are excited. For 2.2-29, the opposite is true, and in the intermediate states the target is in its ground state, only the incident particle being excited.

To set up a useful system of successive approximations, we must combine 2.2-23 and 2.2-30. By analogy with 2.1-18 and 2.1-22, it is possible to define an operator

$$t_i = v_i + v_i\alpha Gv_i + v_i\alpha Gv_i\alpha Gv_i + \cdots$$
$$= v_i + v_i\alpha G(E)t_i. \qquad (2.2\text{-}31)$$

This represents the scattering of the incident particle by the ith nucleon. The operator t_i is not equal to the transition operator T (equation 2.1-18) owing to the presence of $\alpha G(E)$. The two become equal only at high energies, as is shown in the following section.

Insertion of the series 2.2-29 for K into 2.2-26 gives the result

$$\langle \mathbf{U} \rangle = \langle L \rangle. \qquad (2.2\text{-}32)$$

From equations 2.2-30 and 2.2-31, we have

$$\langle \mathbf{U} \rangle = \Big\langle \sum_i t_i + \sum_i \sum_{j \neq i} t_i\alpha Gt_j + \cdots \Big\rangle. \qquad (2.2\text{-}33)$$

This expansion forms the basis of a system of successive approximations, and the physical content of the different terms is of some relevance. The second term represents a process in which the incident particle is first scattered by the jth nucleon into an intermediate state in which both the particle and the target nucleus are excited. De-excitation of the target nucleus occurs when the incident particle is scattered by the ith nucleon, where $i \neq j$. This is a process in which a total of three particles are closely involved, and the term in 2.2-33 representing it is known as a three-body cluster. Further terms in the series represent clusters involving four or more particles, including the incident particle. A more complete discussion will be given in the following section.

A different method of calculating the transition amplitude or operator for the same problem has been presented by Kerman, McManus, and Thaler (1959). The starting point of this development is the equation for the transition operator, which results from operating on the left-hand side of 2.2-04 with the total interaction V,

$$T \mid \mu_0 , \mathbf{k} \rangle = (V + VGT) \mid \mu_0 , \mathbf{k} \rangle. \qquad (2.2\text{-}34)$$

Kerman et al. noted that the matrix element of an operator v_i, the interaction between the incident particle and a target nucleon labelled by i, when taken between antisymmetrized states of the target nucleus must be independent of the subscript i. Thus equations 2.2-23 and 2.2-34 may be replaced by

$$T = Av(1 + G\,(E)T)$$
$$= Av + AvGAv + \cdots , \qquad (2.2\text{-}35)$$

where A is the target mass number. Instead of equation 2.2-31, the operator describing the scattering of the incident particle by a nucleon is defined to be

$$\tau = v + vG\tau$$
$$= v + vGv + \cdots . \qquad (2.2\text{-}36)$$

From equations 2.2-35 and 2.2-36, we have

$$T = A\tau + A(A - 1)\tau G\tau + \cdots . \qquad (2.2\text{-}37)$$

This can be simplified by defining a new transition operator

$$T' = \left(1 - \frac{1}{A}\right) T. \qquad (2.2\text{-}38)$$

The operator T' is given by the series

$$T' = U^{(0)} + U^{(0)}GU^{(0)} + \cdots, \qquad (2.2\text{-}39)$$

where we have defined

$$U^{(0)} = (A - 1)\tau. \qquad (2.2\text{-}40)$$

In order to approximate the elastic amplitude, Kerman et al. retain only those terms in 2.2-39 in which all the matrix elements of $U^{(0)}$ are diagonal in the ground state of the target nucleus. This approximation is one of neglecting three-particle and higher clusters. The matrix element of the single-particle potential defined by Kerman et al. is therefore equal to

$$(A - 1)\langle \mu_0, \mathbf{k}'' \mid \tau \mid \mu_0, \mathbf{k}' \rangle \qquad (2.2\text{-}41)$$

for states $\mathbf{k}''$ and $\mathbf{k}'$ of the incident particle.

For complete discussions of high energy expansions for the optical model operator we refer to the papers of Watson (1957) and of Kerman, McManus, and Thaler (1959) which, in addition, both contain references to previous work.

If the incident particle is a nucleon, one difficult point of principle remains. The antisymmetrization of this particle and the target nucleons leads to some difficulty in defining the origin of the optical model potential. If there is no antisymmetrization of the incident particle, it is reasonable that the origin of the optical model potential should coincide with the centre of mass of the target nucleus for any value of A, the target mass number. This assumption is made in all phenomenological optical model analyses of elastic scattering. If the incident nucleon is antisymmetrized, it is reasonable to require that all $A+1$ nucleons should have a common single-particle potential with a specified origin. However, owing to the recoil of the target of A nucleons, this does not seem to be possible.

2.3 Properties of the High Energy Expansion

In this section we shall describe, in greater detail, the properties of the expansion 2.2-33 for the optical model operator **U**.

The first part of the section will cover the properties of the first two terms in the series. At higher energies, there is evidence that the series is usefully convergent, the first term giving a good approximation to the optical model potential. This evidence is presented in Section 3.2. The partial evaluation of the first two terms is part of the content of this section. The important points are that individual terms in the series are slowly and smoothly varying functions of the energy of the incident particle, and that given the size of the target nucleus, and the interaction of the incident particle with a single free nucleon, it is possible to predict the approximate radial extent of the optical model potential and the values of the real and imaginary parts. The convergence of the series therefore leads to a justification, at high energies, of the phenomenological optical model.

In the latter part of the section, we shall examine some of the properties of the whole series 2.2-33, particularly the problem of its convergence. It is shown that when the energy of the incident particle is very low, there are energy regions in which the series cannot be uniformly convergent. The series is exact apart from the failure to antisymmetrize where necessary, and the lack of uniform convergence means only that the basic set of states we have used (2.2-01 and 2.2-02) is not suitable for the energy region in question.

Let us evaluate the first term in the series. The matrix element of the optical model operator is

$$\langle \mathbf{k}' \mid \mathbf{U} \mid \mathbf{k} \rangle \;=\; \langle \mu_0, \mathbf{k}' \mid \sum_i t_i \mid \mu_0, \mathbf{k} \rangle, \qquad (2.3\text{-}01)$$

where $\mathbf{k}$ is the initial, and $\mathbf{k}'$ the final momentum in the centre of mass system of the particle and the nucleus (the many-body centre of mass system). If the ground state wave function of the target nucleus is completely antisymmetrized, all the terms in the sum over the subscript i are equal, and it is correct to calculate the matrix element for scattering by one nucleon with a given momentum coordinate $\mathbf{p}$ in the nucleus and then multiply the result by A to obtain 2.3-01. It can be seen that this method is correct by choosing the ground state wave function to be a determinant of independent particle wave functions. The first approximation we have to make is to replace t (or τ) by t_0, the transition operator for the scattering of two free nucleons. This is known as the impulse approximation (Chew and Wick, 1952; Chew and Goldberger, 1952). When account is taken of spin and isotopic spin, matrix elements of t_0 are represented by linear combinations of different terms each of which is a function of momentum transfer and of momentum in the two-nucleon centre of mass system. Further details of this representation will be given in Section 3.2, but for the present, we shall require only the general form of matrix elements of t_0. The right-hand side of 2.3-01 is

$$\frac{A}{(2\pi)^{3A+3}} \iiint d\xi \, d\mathbf{p} \, d\mathbf{p}' \, \psi_{\mu_0}^*(\xi, \mathbf{p}') \langle \mathbf{p}', \mathbf{k}' \mid t_0 \mid \mathbf{p}, \mathbf{k} \rangle$$
$$\cdot \psi_{\mu_0}(\xi, \mathbf{p}), \quad (2.3\text{-}02)$$

where $\mathbf{p}$ and $\mathbf{p}'$ are the initial and final values of the nucleon momentum coordinate selected. The symbol ξ denotes the remaining $A - 1$ momentum coordinates which we assume to be unchanged by the collision. If the incident nucleon is fast, we can approximate by neglecting any dependence on the motion of the target nucleons, and obtain

$$\langle \mathbf{p}', \mathbf{k}' \mid t_0 \mid \mathbf{p}, \mathbf{k} \rangle = \langle \mathbf{k}' \mid t_0 \mid \mathbf{k} \rangle \delta(\mathbf{p}' + \mathbf{k}' - \mathbf{p} - \mathbf{k}). \quad (2.3\text{-}03)$$

Substituting this in 2.3-02, we have

$$\frac{A}{(2\pi)^{3A}} \iint d\xi \, d\mathbf{p} \, \psi_{\mu_0}^*(\xi, \mathbf{p} - \mathbf{q}) \langle \mathbf{k}' \mid t_0 \mid \mathbf{k} \rangle \psi_{\mu_0}(\xi, \mathbf{p}), \quad (2.3\text{-}04)$$

where $\mathbf{q} = \mathbf{k}' - \mathbf{k}$ is the momentum transfer. Substitution of the Fourier transforms of the momentum wave functions

$$\psi_{\mu_0}^*(\xi, \mathbf{p} - \mathbf{q}) = \iint d\mathbf{n} \, d\mathbf{r} \, \psi_{\mu_0}^*(\mathbf{n}, \mathbf{r}) \, e^{i(\mathbf{p}-\mathbf{q})\cdot\mathbf{r} + i\xi\cdot\mathbf{n}} \quad (2.3\text{-}05)$$

and

$$\psi_{\mu 0}(\xi, \mathbf{p}) = \iint d\mathbf{n}' \, d\mathbf{r}' \, \psi_{\mu 0}(\mathbf{n}', \mathbf{r}') \, e^{-i(\mathbf{p}\cdot\mathbf{r}' + \xi\cdot\mathbf{n}')} \quad (2.3\text{-}06)$$

into 2.3-04 results in

$$\langle \mathbf{k}' \mid \mathbf{U} \mid \mathbf{k} \rangle = A \langle \mathbf{k}' \mid t_0 \mid \mathbf{k} \rangle \iint d\mathbf{n} \, d\mathbf{r} \, e^{-i\mathbf{q}\cdot\mathbf{r}} \mid \psi_{\mu 0}(\mathbf{n}, \mathbf{r}) \mid^2, \quad (2.3\text{-}07)$$

where we have used the identity

$$\delta(\mathbf{n} - \mathbf{n}') = \frac{1}{(2\pi)^{3A-3}} \int d\xi \, e^{i\xi\cdot(\mathbf{n}-\mathbf{n}')} \quad (2.3\text{-}08)$$

Integrating over the coordinates $\mathbf{n}$, we have

$$\langle \mathbf{k}' \mid \mathbf{U} \mid \mathbf{k} \rangle = A \langle \mathbf{k}' \mid t_0 \mid \mathbf{k} \rangle \int d\mathbf{r} \, \rho(\mathbf{r}) \, e^{-i\mathbf{q}\cdot\mathbf{r}}, \quad (2.3\text{-}09)$$

where $A\rho$ is the nucleon density distribution, ρ being normalised by the relation

$$\int d\mathbf{r} \, \rho(\mathbf{r}) = 1. \quad (2.3\text{-}10)$$

We can write the matrix element of $\mathbf{U}$ in terms of a local and energy dependent potential $U(\mathbf{k},\mathbf{r})$, although we shall show in Section 2.8 that the potential must be both nonlocal and energy dependent. Thus,

$$\langle \mathbf{k}' \mid \mathbf{U} \mid \mathbf{k} \rangle = \int d\mathbf{r}' \, U(k, \mathbf{r}') \, e^{-i\mathbf{q}\cdot\mathbf{r}'}. \quad (2.3\text{-}11)$$

From 2.3-09 and 2.3-10 and with $q = 0$, we have

$$\int d\mathbf{r}' \, U(k, \mathbf{r}') = A \langle \mathbf{k} \mid t_0 \mid \mathbf{k} \rangle, \quad (2.3\text{-}12)$$

which shows that the volume integral of the potential is very simply related to the nucleon-nucleon forward scattering amplitude.

Equation 2.3-11 means that the matrix element 2.3-09 is the Fourier transform of the potential. Therefore, in order to calculate the potential, we have to form the Fourier transform of 2.3-09

$$U(k, \mathbf{r}) = \frac{A}{(2\pi)^3} \int d\mathbf{q} \langle \mathbf{k}' \mid t_0 \mid \mathbf{k} \rangle F(\mathbf{q}) \, e^{i\mathbf{q}\cdot\mathbf{r}}, \quad (2.3\text{-}13)$$

where the nuclear form factor is defined by

$$F(\mathbf{q}) = \int d\mathbf{r} \rho\,(\mathbf{r})\, e^{-i\mathbf{q}\cdot\mathbf{r}}. \qquad (2.3\text{-}14)$$

For the approximation of taking the nucleon-nucleon amplitude to be independent of the momentum transfer, we have

$$U(k, \mathbf{r}) = A \langle \mathbf{k} \mid t_0 \mid \mathbf{k} \rangle \rho(\mathbf{r}). \qquad (2.3\text{-}15)$$

Equation 2.3-15 gives a potential which is suitable for predicting the scattering at very small values of the momentum transfer. In this approximation, which is the simplest possible, both real and imaginary parts of the optical model potential have the same shape and size as the density distribution of the target nucleus. The more general case (equation 2.3-13) gives a potential which does not have the same shape as the nuclear density distribution. Furthermore, the real and imaginary parts need not have the same radial extent.

In order to complete our discussion of the first term in 2.2-33, we have to derive one further result. To start with, the transition amplitude for the scattering of two free nonrelativistic particles is invariant under coordinate transformations (Møller, 1945). Therefore, from equation 2.1-21, the forward scattering amplitude for two nucleons in their centre of mass system is related to the transition amplitude by

$$f(0) = -\frac{m}{4\pi} \langle \mathbf{k} \mid t_0 \mid \mathbf{k} \rangle, \qquad (2.3\text{-}16)$$

where m is here the nucleon mass. The optical theorem relates the imaginary part of 2.3-16 to the nucleon-nucleon total cross section,

$$\operatorname{Im} f(0) = \frac{m\sigma \mid \mathbf{v} \mid}{8\pi}, \qquad (2.3\text{-}17)$$

v being the relative velocity. From equations 2.3-15, 2.3-16, and 2.3-17, the imaginary part of the potential is

$$-\mathrm{Im}\, U(k, \mathbf{r}) \equiv W(k, \mathbf{r}) = \tfrac{1}{2} A\sigma \,|\, \mathbf{v} \,|\, \rho(\mathbf{r}). \qquad (2.3\text{-}18)$$

Equation 2.3-18 has been used in the introduction (Section 1.1). This equation does not take into account the fact that the struck nucleon in the target must obey the exclusion principle. The importance of the exclusion principle in this context, when the energy of the incident particle is low, has been demonstrated by Lane and Wandel (1955).

The problem of the validity of the impulse approximation can be investigated by comparing equation 2.2-31 with the equation satisfied by t_0,

$$t_0 = v + vG_0 t_0. \qquad (2.3\text{-}19)$$

By iteration of both equations, we have

$$t = t_0 + t_0 \{ \alpha G - G_0 \} t$$
$$\approx t_0 + t_0 \{ \alpha G - G_0 \} t_0. \qquad (2.3\text{-}20)$$

This equation has been investigated by Kerman, McManus, and Thaler (1959). A different way of investigating the validity of the impulse approximation is the comparison, with experiment, of the differential cross section and polarization calculated from the potential 2.3-13. This is described in Section 3.2. The developments of the present section can also be applied directly to the optical model operator given by equation 2.2-40.

Evaluation of the second term in the expansion 2.2-33 leads to more complicated formulae. Substituting for α according to equation 2.2-25, we have, for a given nucleon pair (i, j),

$$t_i \alpha G t_j = t_i G t_j - t_i \beta G t_j. \qquad (2.3\text{-}21)$$

For simplicity, the collisions with the two nucleons can be described by the impulse approximation as in the first part of this section, the operator t_i being replaced by t_0. This approximation does not affect the way in which 2.3-21 depends on the detailed structure of the target nucleus.

From equations 2.1-08 and 2.3-21, the contribution to the matrix element of the optical model operator $\langle \mathbf{k}' \mid \mathbf{U} \mid \mathbf{k} \rangle$ is, for one pair (i, j),

$$\frac{1}{(2\pi)^3} \sum_{\mu} \int d\mathbf{k}'' \frac{\langle \mu_0, \mathbf{k}' \mid t_0 \mid \mu, \mathbf{k}'' \rangle \langle \mu, \mathbf{k}'' \mid t_0 \mid \mu_0, \mathbf{k} \rangle}{E - E_1(\mu) - E_2(k'') + i\epsilon}$$

$$-\frac{1}{(2\pi)^3} \int d\mathbf{k}'' \frac{\langle \mu_0, \mathbf{k}' \mid t_0 \mid \mu_0, \mathbf{k}'' \rangle \langle \mu_0, \mathbf{k}'' \mid t_0 \mid \mu_0, \mathbf{k} \rangle}{E - E_1(\mu_0) - E_2(k'') + i\epsilon}.$$

$$(2.3-22)$$

With no consideration of spin and isotopic spin states, a matrix element in 2.3-22 is of the form

$$\langle \mu_0, \mathbf{k}' \mid t_0 \mid \mu, \mathbf{k}'' \rangle = \int d\mathbf{r}_i \, \rho_{\mu 0, \mu}(\mathbf{r}_i) \langle \mathbf{k}' \mid t_0 \mid \mathbf{k}'' \rangle \, e^{-i\mathbf{q}_i \cdot \mathbf{r}_i} \quad (2.3-23)$$

(see equation 2.3-07), the nucleon density being replaced by

$$\rho_{\mu 0, \mu}(\mathbf{r}_i) = \iint d\mathbf{n} \, d\mathbf{r}_j \, \psi_{\mu 0}^*(\mathbf{n}, \mathbf{r}_i, \mathbf{r}_j) \psi_{\mu}(\mathbf{n}, \mathbf{r}_i, \mathbf{r}_j). \quad (2.3-24)$$

The coordinate of the target nucleon with which the collision takes place is $\mathbf{r}_i$. The other collision is with the nucleon having coordinate $\mathbf{r}_j$, and in this case the symbol $\mathbf{n}$ represents the remaining $A - 2$ target coordinates. The momentum transfer is $\mathbf{q}_i = \mathbf{k}' - \mathbf{k}''$. The target wave functions are complete,

$$\sum_{\mu} \psi_{\mu}(\mathbf{n}, \mathbf{r}_i, \mathbf{r}_j) \psi_{\mu}^*(\mathbf{n}', \mathbf{r}_i', \mathbf{r}_j') = \delta(\mathbf{n} - \mathbf{n}')\delta(\mathbf{r}_i - \mathbf{r}_i')\delta(\mathbf{r}_j - \mathbf{r}_j'),$$

$$(2.3-25)$$

and this leads to the sum rule

$$\sum_{\mu} \rho_{\mu 0, \mu}(\mathbf{r}_i) \rho_{\mu, \mu 0}(\mathbf{r}_j') = \rho_{\mu 0, \mu 0}(\mathbf{r}_i, \mathbf{r}_j'), \quad (2.3-26)$$

where

$$\rho_{\mu 0, \mu 0}(\mathbf{r}_i, \mathbf{r}_j') = \int d\mathbf{n} \mid \psi_{\mu 0}(\mathbf{n}, \mathbf{r}_i, \mathbf{r}_j') \mid^2. \quad (2.3-27)$$

The quantity

$$\rho_{\mu 0, \mu 0}(\mathbf{r}_i , \mathbf{r}_j') \, d\mathbf{r}_i \, d\mathbf{r}_j'$$

is the probability that the ith and jth nucleons are in volume elements $d\mathbf{r}_i$ and $d\mathbf{r}_j'$, respectively, the other $A - 2$ nucleons being unrestricted. In order to simplify 2.3-22, we can approximate very roughly by neglecting the excitation of the target. The two denominators in 2.3-22 are then equal. With the results 2.3-23 and 2.3-26, the contribution 2.3-22 becomes

$$\frac{1}{(2\pi)^3} \iiint d\mathbf{k}'' \, d\mathbf{r}_i \, d\mathbf{r}_j \frac{\langle \mathbf{k}' \mid t_0 \mid \mathbf{k}'' \rangle \langle \mathbf{k}'' \mid t_0 \mid \mathbf{k} \rangle}{E - E_1(\mu_0) - E_2(k'') + i\epsilon}$$

$$\exp(-i\mathbf{q}_i \cdot \mathbf{r}_i - i\mathbf{q}_j \cdot \mathbf{r}_j)$$

$$\{\rho_{\mu 0, \mu 0}(\mathbf{r}_i , \mathbf{r}_j) - \rho_{\mu 0, \mu 0}(\mathbf{r}_i)\rho_{\mu 0, \mu 0}(\mathbf{r}_j)\}. \quad (2.3\text{-}28)$$

The term 2.3-28 depends on the structure of the target nucleus through the quantity contained in the brackets, which is a measure of the extent to which the nucleons are correlated in pairs. In a real nucleus the strong short-range nucleon-nucleon interaction, and to a lesser extent the antisymmetrization, lead to a very considerable pair correlation. For a large target nucleus, it is useful to define the pair correlation function C,

$$\rho_{\mu 0, \mu 0}(\mathbf{r}_i , \mathbf{r}_j) = \rho_{\mu 0, \mu 0}(\mathbf{r}_i)\rho_{\mu 0, \mu 0}(\mathbf{r}_j)\{1 + C(\mathbf{r}_i - \mathbf{r}_j)\}. \quad (2.3\text{-}29)$$

Then the important term in 2.3-28 is equal to

$$\rho_{\mu 0, \mu 0}(\mathbf{r}_i)\rho_{\mu 0, \mu 0}(\mathbf{r}_j)C(\mathbf{r}_i - \mathbf{r}_j), \quad (2.3\text{-}30)$$

and 2.3-21 depends directly on C. A more complete discussion of the pair correlation function may be found in the paper by Watson (1958).

The partial evaluation of 2.3-21 carried out in this section is sufficient to show that the term depends on the target pair correlation function. It is so approximate, however, that it could not be a rigorous test of the useful convergence of the series 2.2-33. The assumption of convergence is justified by comparison of the potential 2.3-13 with the phenomenological potential which fits the experimental differential cross sections and polarizations for high energy nucleons.   This is described in Section 3.2.

The simplification of the description of the whole scattering process, made possible by the optical model operator, is shown by the form of the elastic scattering state vector.   This is (equation 2.2-08)

$$| \Phi \rangle = (1 + \beta G U + \beta G U \beta G U + \cdots) | \mu_0, \mathbf{k} \rangle. \quad (2.3\text{-}31)$$

Approximating $\mathbf{U}$ by the first term in 2.2-33, the state vector becomes

$$| \Phi \rangle = (1 + \sum_i \beta G t_i + \sum_i \sum_j \beta G t_i \beta G t_j + \cdots) | \mu_0, \mathbf{k} \rangle.$$
$$(2.3\text{-}32)$$

This represents a series of multiple scattering processes.   The presence of the projection operator β shows that between collisions with the separate nucleons (denoted by the operators t_i), the incident particle may be excited, but the target is in its ground state.   The exact elastic scattering amplitude is

$$\langle \mu_0, \mathbf{k}' | \{ \mathbf{U} + \mathbf{U} \beta G \mathbf{U} + \cdots \} | \mu_0, \mathbf{k} \rangle. \quad (2.3\text{-}33)$$

Making the approximation of equation 2.3-32, this becomes

$$\langle \mu_0, \mathbf{k}' | \{ \sum_i t_i + \sum_i \sum_j t_i \beta G t_j + \cdots \} | \mu_0, \mathbf{k} \rangle. \quad (2.3\text{-}34)$$

This shows the class of multiple scattering processes which is included if the approximation of equation 2.3-01 is made. The numerical solution of the Schrödinger equation including the calculated optical model potential 2.3-13 is therefore equivalent to calculating the entire series of multiple scattering processes contained in 2.3-34.

It is of interest to know how to determine the relative importance of successive terms in the series 2.3-34.   The rule for doing this follows from the one-to-one correspondence between terms in the two series 2.3-33 and 2.3-34.   The series 2.3-33 is just the Born series, as may be seen by comparison with 2.1-22. Therefore, if it is known that the scattering amplitude may be calculated accurately from the optical model potential by the first Born approximation, then it is clear that there can be little multiple scattering and the first term in 2.3-34 is sufficient. Similarly, the importance of the second Born approximation, $U\beta GU$, in 2.3-33, is a measure of the importance of multiple scattering processes consisting of two collisions. We expect that when the Born series is not convergent, an expansion of the state vector $|\Phi\rangle$ into the multiple scattering processes of 2.3-32 will not be convergent either. The problem of convergence does not arise though, in the numerical solution of the Schrödinger equation including the optical model potential. For completeness, we note that the studies of the convergence of the Born series for a local, static, potential (for example, Davies, 1960) are not strictly applicable to the series 2.3-33 because the optical model potential is of a more general form; it is both nonlocal and dependent on the energy of the incident particle.

The convergence of the various other series we have employed must be considered. First of all, the convergence of the series 2.2-31 for the operator t_i represents no serious problem. Even if the series is not uniformly convergent in the energy range considered, the operator t_i may still be calculated from v_i by the closed (integral) equation 2.2-31. If v_i is represented by a potential having a hard core, the terms in the series 2.2-31 do not exist (they are all infinite), and furthermore, the closed form cannot be used directly. Under these circumstances, it is necessary to consider that part of the wave function for the two particles which is a function of their relative coordinate.[3]

[3] The procedure has been given by Bethe and Goldstone (1957). Applying it, for example, to the two-body problem, we should consider equation 2.1-19 for the wave function. An expansion of the wave function (equation 1.3-03) into partial wave functions would give a set of integral equations, one for each value of l. The products $v(r)\phi_l(kr)$ occur in the integrand, and are singular at the hard core boundary, $r = r_c$. The product may be written as

$$v(r)\phi_l(kr) = b_l\delta(r - r_c) + v(r)\phi_l(kr)\theta(r - r_c),$$

where the step function θ is unity if its argument is positive, and zero if

Nonconvergence of the cluster expansion 2.2-33, however, is important and corresponds to a situation of physical interest. We can show that there are energy regions for which the series cannot be uniformly convergent. Let ΔE be the energy difference between the ground and first excited states of the target nucleus. If the incident particle is sufficiently slow so that the centre of mass energy (excluding rest masses) is less than ΔE, then from equation 2.1-08 and the definition of α it can be seen that each term in the series 2.2-33 must lead to a real potential, provided ϵ is infinitesimal. The potential can have an imaginary part only when the centre of mass energy is greater than the threshold energy ΔE and there is inelastic scattering to the first or higher excited states of the target nucleus. Although the series 2.2-33 is exact apart from the failure to antisymmetrize the incident particle if it is a nucleon, the predictions just made are not in agreement with the experimental situation. A slow neutron colliding with a medium or heavy nucleus can produce a compound nucleus with a high excitation energy, usually of the order of 8 Mev. At this excitation energy there will certainly be many compound nucleus levels which can be formed by incident neutrons which are not sufficiently fast to give inelastic scattering to the first excited state of the target. Most of these compound nucleus levels can decay to give reactions of the form (n, γ), or possibly (n, α), so that the reaction cross section is not zero. The optical model potential for neutrons in this energy region must therefore have an imaginary part. A further important point is that the separate terms of the cluster expansion have a smooth variation with energy.[4] The cross sections predicted

---

it is zero or negative. The coefficient b_l is determined by the boundary condition that $\phi_l(kr_c) = 0$. The integral equation is then simply a Fredholm equation of the second kind, which may be solved by standard methods (for example, Fox and Goodwin, 1953).

[4] The energy derivative of $\mathbf{U}$ may be found by noting the formal result

$$\frac{\partial t_i}{\partial E} = -t_i(E - H_1 - H_2 + i\epsilon)^{-2}t_i.$$

by the potential should therefore be smoothly varying functions of energy. However, the experimental cross sections for a given target nucleus vary rapidly when the energy of the incident particle is low.

The disagreement we have outlined means that the cluster expansion 2.2-33 is not uniformly convergent. This nonconvergence may also extend to some energy regions beyond the first threshold for inelastic scattering. That the cluster expansion is not uniformly convergent means only that the basic set of states (2.2-01 and 2.2-02) we have used is not suitable for the energy region in question. In the low energy region, a different basic set of states is necessary, and this forms the subject of Sections 2.4 and 2.5.

The nonconvergence of the expansion 2.2-33 when the energy is in the region of a discrete level of the compound nucleus may be compared with the time-dependent picture of Friedman and Weisskopf (1955). The failure of the expansion to converge is a formal expression of the fact that the incident particle, neglecting antisymmetrization, is contained in the compound nucleus for a time long compared with the time $\hbar U^{-1} \approx 10^{-23}$ second characteristic of scattering through the first term in the expansion only, which is known as scattering by direct interaction.

An alternative formulation of the optical model has been presented by Feshbach (1958a). The generalised optical model operator defined by Feshbach, as a function of energy, contains poles which correspond to the discrete levels of the compound nucleus. When the energy is in the neighbourhood of one of the poles in the potential, the scattering amplitude has the expected Breit-Wigner dispersion form.

2.4 Dispersion Formulae for Potential Scattering

The basic set of states defined by Kapur and Peierls (1938) is a useful starting point for a theory of the optical model when the incident particle is of low energy. In the first part of this section, an account is given of the application of the formalism to the two-body problem. The section is completed by a short account of other dispersion formulae. The extension of the Kapur-Peierls dispersion formula to many-particle systems is described in the following section. In the first part, we shall follow the presentations of Kapur and Peierls (1938) and of Brown (1959).

The two-body problem has reduced mass M and centre of mass energy E. The $l = 0$ partial wave function satisfies

$$\frac{d^2\phi}{dr^2} + 2M(E - U)\phi = 0, \qquad (2.4\text{-}01)$$

where $U(r)$ is a velocity-independent potential of short range, for the present assumed to be real. A basic feature of the formalism is the definition of a sphere, of radius $r = R$, which completely encloses the interaction potential. For $r > R$, the partial wave function satisfies

$$\frac{d^2\phi}{dr^2} + k^2\phi = 0, \qquad (2.4\text{-}02)$$

where

$$k^2 = 2ME. \qquad (2.4\text{-}03)$$

From 1.2-01 and 1.3-03, the scattering solution of equation 2.4-02 is

$$\phi = i\sqrt{\pi}\{e^{-ikr} - Se^{ikr}\}. \qquad (2.4\text{-}04)$$

In both this section and the following one, the subscripts denoting the angular momentum value are omitted. For $r < R$, ϕ may be expanded in terms of the Kapur-Peierls eigenfunctions ϕ_λ,

$$\phi = \sum_\lambda a_\lambda \phi_\lambda, \qquad (2.4\text{-}05)$$

where the a_λ are constants. The ϕ_λ are the solutions of the equation

$$\frac{d^2\phi_\lambda}{dr^2} + 2M(E_\lambda - U)\phi_\lambda = 0 \qquad (2.4\text{-}06)$$

in the interval $(0,R)$ which are zero at the origin and satisfy the boundary condition

$$\left\{\frac{d\phi_\lambda}{dr}\right\}_{r=R} = ik\phi_\lambda(R), \qquad (2.4\text{-}07)$$

where k is defined by equation 2.4-03.

Comparison with equation 2.4-04 shows that a boundary condition of the type 2.4-07 can never be satisfied by a physical partial wave function ϕ. To satisfy the condition, ϕ would need to contain only the outgoing wave component e^{ikr}. This difference in boundary conditions shows that the expansion 2.4-05 requires justification. This is contained in the papers by Kapur and Peierls (1938) and Peierls (1948). In this section we shall assume that 2.4-05 is valid.

The condition 2.4-07 and the boundary condition at the origin lead to a discrete spectrum of eigenvalues E_λ. The nature of the eigenvalues and eigenfunctions is made more clear by looking at the special problem in which $k = 0$ and $U(r)$ is a square well potential of radius R. With these restrictions, the eigenfunctions are real,

$$\phi_\lambda = \left(\frac{2}{R}\right)^{1/2} \sin K_\lambda r, \qquad (2.4\text{-}08)$$

and the eigenvalues are given by

$$K_\lambda R = (\lambda + \tfrac{1}{2})\pi, \qquad (2.4\text{-}09)$$

where $\lambda = 0, 1, 2, \cdots$, and

$$K_\lambda^2 = 2M(E_\lambda - U). \qquad (2.4\text{-}10)$$

The eigenvalues E_λ are real and are the energies at which $l = 0$ resonances would occur in the scattering cross section. The subscript λ denotes the number of radial nodes of the partial wave function in the square well. In the general problem, $k > 0$, the spectrum is discrete, but the eigenvalues and eigenfunctions are complex. For every value of k, there exists a distinct and complete set of eigenvalues and eigenfunctions.

The completeness of the eigenfunctions for the general problem
has been proved by Peierls (1948).

The eigenfunctions are orthogonal and can be normalised.
The condition is

$$\int_0^R \phi_\lambda(r)\phi_{\lambda'}(r)\ dr = \delta_{\lambda\lambda'}, \qquad (2.4\text{-}11)$$

which results because all the eigenfunctions obey the same
boundary condition at $r = R$. The proof of equation 2.4-11
depends on integrating by parts

$$\int_0^R \left\{ \phi_{\lambda'} \frac{d^2\phi_\lambda}{dr^2} - \phi_\lambda \frac{d^2\phi_{\lambda'}}{dr^2} \right\} dr = \left\{ \phi_{\lambda'} \frac{d\phi_\lambda}{dr} - \phi_\lambda \frac{d\phi_{\lambda'}}{dr} \right\}_{r=R} = 0,$$
$$(2.4\text{-}12)$$

owing to the boundary condition 2.4-07.

The first problem is the calculation of the coefficients a_λ
in the expansion 2.4-05. From equations 2.4-01, 2.4-06, and
2.4-11 we have

$$\int_0^R \left\{ \phi_\lambda \frac{d^2\phi}{dr^2} - \phi \frac{d^2\phi_\lambda}{dr^2} \right\} dr = -2M(E - E_\lambda)a_\lambda. \quad (2.4\text{-}13)$$

By partial integration, the left-hand side of 2.4-13 equals

$$\left\{ \phi_\lambda \frac{d\phi}{dr} - \phi \frac{d\phi_\lambda}{dr} \right\}_{r=R} = \phi_\lambda(R) \left\{ \frac{d\phi}{dr} - ik\phi \right\}_{r=R}$$
$$= 2k\sqrt{\pi}\ \phi_\lambda(R)\ e^{-ikR} \qquad (2.4\text{-}14)$$

Therefore, from 2.4-13 and 2.4-14,

$$a_\lambda = -\frac{k\sqrt{\pi}}{M(E - E_\lambda)}\ \phi_\lambda(R)\ e^{-ikR}. \qquad (2.4\text{-}15)$$

The second step is the calculation of S. Equating the exterior and interior wave functions, 2.4-04 and 2.4-05, at $r = R$,
we have

$$S = e^{-2ikR} \left\{ 1 - i \sum_\lambda \frac{\Gamma_\lambda}{E - E_\lambda} \right\}, \qquad (2.4\text{-}16)$$

where the quantity Γ_λ is defined by

$$\Gamma_\lambda = \frac{k}{M} \phi_\lambda^2(R), \qquad (2.4\text{-}17)$$

and is known as the width, although it is complex and not real.

The first part of the right-hand side of equation 2.4-16 is e^{-2ikr}. As the phase shift for scattering by a hard sphere of radius R is $\delta = -kR$, this is known as the hard sphere part of S. Equation 2.4-16 is the main result of this section; it represents the scattering parameter S in terms of the Kapur-Peierls eigenfunctions and eigenvalues. At zero energy, the interpretation is simple because the eigenvalues are real and are the energies at which $l = 0$ resonances occur in the scattering system. The result is a representation of the scattering amplitude in terms of the resonances. The important point is that the formalism is exact, and unlike Section 2.2, does not rely on expansions which may not be uniformly convergent. The scattering cross section can be calculated from S by equation 1.2-02.

The imaginary part of E_λ can be calculated by considering equation 2.4-06 and its complex conjugate. Let E_λ be

$$E_\lambda = e_\lambda - iw_\lambda . \qquad (2.4\text{-}18)$$

We have,

$$\int_0^R \left\{ \phi_\lambda \frac{d^2 \phi_\lambda^*}{dr^2} - \phi_\lambda^* \frac{d^2 \phi_\lambda}{dr^2} \right\} dr = -4iMw_\lambda \int_0^R |\phi_\lambda|^2 \, dr, \quad (2.4\text{-}19)$$

and by partial integration and the boundary condition 2.4-07, the left-hand side is

$$-2ik \, |\phi_\lambda(R)|^2 ,$$

so that

$$w_\lambda = \frac{k}{2M} \frac{|\phi_\lambda(R)|^2}{\int_0^R |\phi_\lambda|^2 \, dr} . \qquad (2.4\text{-}20)$$

For small values of k, the boundary condition 2.4-07 is nearly the same as the condition

$$\left\{\frac{d\phi_\lambda}{dr}\right\}_{r=R} = 0,$$

and therefore the ϕ_λ and the width Γ_λ will be very nearly real. For small values of k, an estimate of the imaginary part of E_λ may be made by substituting in 2.4-20 the real eigenfunctions 2.4-08. The estimate leads to

$$w_\lambda^{-1} = \frac{MR}{k}, \qquad (2.4\text{-}21)$$

which is the radius of the potential divided by the velocity of the incident particle. This is the lifetime associated with the eigenfunction ϕ_λ. Let us consider the scattering of a neutron by a nucleus of intermediate mass number. Then if $R = 5 \times 10^{-13}$ cm and $E = 0.25$ Mev, the time (2.4-21) is 0.7×10^{-21} seconds, and the imaginary part of E_λ roughly 1.0 Mev. This justifies the assertion made in Section 1.1 that potential models of the nucleus lead only to broad resonances.

The extension of the method to values of l greater than zero has been given by Kapur and Peierls and by Brown.

An estimate of Γ_λ can be made by the method outlined for w_λ. Equation 2.4-17 gives

$$\Gamma_\lambda = \frac{2k}{MR}, \qquad (2.4\text{-}22)$$

and therefore the imaginary part of the eigenvalue is equal to half the width, near zero energy, that is

$$w_\lambda = \tfrac{1}{2}\Gamma_\lambda. \qquad (2.4\text{-}23)$$

The problem in which the potential is complex has been considered by Brown (1957 and 1959). The solution is particularly simple for square well potentials where both real and imaginary parts have a radius equal to the matching radius R. For this special case, equation 2.4-06 can be rearranged into the form

$$\frac{d^2\phi_\lambda}{dr^2} + 2M\{(E_\lambda - iW) - (U - iW)\}\phi_\lambda = 0. \quad (2.4\text{-}24)$$

The eigenvalues for the complex potential $U - iW$ are therefore $E_\lambda - iW$, and the eigenfunctions are the original ϕ_λ. Equation 2.4-16 is replaced by

$$S = e^{-2ikR}\left\{1 - i\sum_\lambda \frac{\Gamma_\lambda}{E - e_\lambda + i(w_\lambda + W)}\right\}, \quad (2.4\text{-}25)$$

if the potential is complex. If E is small and nearly equal to one of the e_λ, the total cross section calculated from 2.4-25 will have the Lorentz shape,

$$\sigma_t \approx \frac{4\pi}{k^2} \frac{w_\lambda(W + w_\lambda)}{(E - e_\lambda)^2 + (W + w_\lambda)^2}. \quad (2.4\text{-}26)$$

The effect of the imaginary part of the potential is to increase the breadth of the maxima in the total cross section; the full width at half height is $2(W + w_\lambda)$. These results will be used in the following two sections.

Dispersion formulae in which the eigenfunctions satisfy boundary conditions different from 2.4-07 have been derived by Siegert (1939), by Wigner and Eisenbud (1947), and by Humblet and Rosenfeld (1961). The Kapur-Peierls dispersion formula 2.4-16, although exact, has an explicit dependence on the matching radius R, and the eigenvalues and eigenfunctions depend on the momentum k through the boundary condition 2.4-07. These disadvantages are not present in the dispersion theory of Siegert and of Humblet and Rosenfeld. Their starting point, for s-wave potential scattering, is the quantity S (equation 2.4-04) considered as a function of the complex momentum k. The function $S(k)$ is meromorphic in the finite plane cut from conjugate points on the imaginary axis to $\pm i\infty$, and the positions of the poles are given by

$$k = k_\lambda \equiv \kappa_\lambda - i\omega_\lambda$$

and

$$k = -k_\lambda^*, \qquad \lambda = 1, 2, 3, \ldots$$

with the conditions,

$$\kappa_\lambda \geq 0; \qquad \omega_\lambda > 0 \quad \text{if} \quad \kappa_\lambda \neq 0.$$

The poles for which $\kappa_\lambda = 0$ lie on the imaginary axis and those on the positive half give the bound states of the system. The remaining poles lie in the lower half plane and give the resonances in the s-wave scattering cross section. The energies

$$E_\lambda = \frac{k_\lambda^2}{2M}$$

are complex eigenvalues of equation 2.4-01, and the corresponding eigenfunctions satisfy the natural boundary condition of having no ingoing spherical waves.

The meromorphic function $S(k)$, and therefore the scattering amplitude, can be calculated from the positions and residues of the poles (see Titchmarsh, 1939, p. 110). If it is assumed that the poles are simple and that the k_λ satisfy the sequence of inequalities

$$0 < |k_1| \leq |k_2| \leq |k_3| \cdots,$$

then the dispersion formula is

$$S = Q + k^M \sum_\lambda \left\{ \frac{b(k_\lambda)}{k_\lambda^M (k - k_\lambda)} + (-1)^M \frac{b(-k_\lambda^*)}{k_\lambda^{*M}(k + k_\lambda^*)} \right\},$$

$$(2.4\text{-}27)$$

where the residues are $b(k_\lambda)$, the function Q is a polynomial of finite degree, and the integer M satisfies $M \geq 1$.

The extension of the method to many-particle systems is described in the paper of Humblet and Rosenfeld. For the application to the optical model, we refer to the paper of Rosenfeld (1961).

The position on the imaginary axis of the branch points referred to above depends on the form of the potential. For certain classes of potential, the cuts are replaced by poles which are known as redundant poles. These further singularities do not affect the dispersion formula 2.4-27; Q is still a slowly varying function of k. For a complete account of these singularities and of the analytic properties of the amplitude for potential scattering we refer to the paper of Martin (1959).

2.5 The Many-body Dispersion Formula

An expansion for the parameter S may be found for the problem in which the nucleus is regarded as a many-particle system. For simplicity, we shall restrict the derivation to s-wave scattering of neutrons. Antisymmetrization of the incident neutron would give no new results (Brown, 1959) and is therefore neglected. The purpose of both this section and the following one is to give a qualitative understanding of the giant resonances which occur at low neutron energies. This justifies the restricted form of the problem considered.

Following Brown (1959), the compound states of the whole system are defined inside and on a sphere of radius R with origin at the centre of mass of the target. This sphere is assumed to enclose the region in which there is any interaction between the incident particle and the target, and therefore those parts of S which are the result of rearrangement collisions, such as the (n, α) reaction, are neglected. We shall call the region inside the sphere the interior region. The wave function for the compound state $| p \rangle$ is denoted by $\Phi^{(p)}(\mathbf{r}, \mathbf{n})$, where $\mathbf{r}$ is the coordinate of the incident neutron and $\mathbf{n}$, in this section, represents the coordinates of the A nucleons in the target. Let $\psi_\mu(\mathbf{n})$ be a complete orthogonal set of eigenfunctions for the target, the ground state being denoted by μ_0. For every value of μ there is a complete set of single-particle Kapur-Peierls eigenfunctions $\phi_{\mu\lambda}(r)$ which satisfy the boundary condition

$$\left\{ \frac{d\phi_{\mu\lambda}}{dr} \right\}_{r=R} = ik_\mu \phi_{\mu\lambda}(R), \qquad (2.5\text{-}01)$$

where k_μ is defined by

$$k_\mu^2 = 2M(E - E_1(\mu)). \qquad (2.5\text{-}02)$$

This means that k_μ corresponds to an energy equal to the difference between the energy E of the incident particle and the excitation energy of the target. The ground state energy of the target, $E_1(\mu_0)$, is taken to be the zero of energy. The compound states may be expanded in terms of these eigenfunctions. Thus,

$$\Phi^{(p)} = \sum_{\mu,\lambda} a^p_{\mu\lambda}\psi_\mu(\mathbf{n})\,\frac{\phi_{\mu\lambda}(r)}{r}\,, \qquad (2.5\text{-}03)$$

where the $a^p_{\mu\lambda}$ are constants. Equation 2.5-03 represents a compound state as a linear combination of the states into which it can decay. Again following Brown (1959, p. 899), we must restrict the sum over the index μ in the expansion 2.5-03 to those states of the target which have low excitation energies and cannot decay by particle emission. The wave functions of these states are completely contained in the interior region. This approximation and the expansion 2.5-03 in terms of known functions, lead to an eigenvalue problem in the interior region. The total Hamiltonian is

$$H = H_1 + H_2 + V \qquad (2.5\text{-}04)$$

(Section 2.2), and the compound states of the whole system satisfy, in the interior region, the equation

$$H\,|\,p\rangle = W_p\,|\,p\rangle \qquad (2.5\text{-}05)$$

where the energies W_p are complex and have negative imaginary parts which are small compared with the $(W + w_\lambda)$ of the Kapur-Peierls single particle eigenvalues.

It is assumed that both the incident neutron and the ground state of the target have zero spin, and therefore that all the compound states $\Phi^{(p)}$ are of zero spin. The eigenfunctions ψ_μ and $\phi_{\mu\lambda}$ in the expansion 2.5-03 are assumed to be of zero spin. It is to be emphasised that these restrictions will not interfere with the nature of the results of this section but will help to simplify the formalism.

From 2.5-03 and 2.5-05 it follows that the compound states

are orthogonal, and may be normalised,

$$\iint_0^R \Phi^{(p)} \, \Phi^{(q)} r^2 \, dr \, d\mathbf{n} = \delta_{pq}, \qquad (2.5\text{-}06)$$

where the domain of integration for the variables $\mathbf{n}$ is the interior region. The variable r is integrated over the interval $(0, R)$. Recoil of the target is not considered.

In the interior region, the scattering state $|\Psi\rangle$ (equation 2.2-04) may be expanded in terms of the compound states. Thus,

$$\Psi(\mathbf{r}, \mathbf{n}) = \sum_p a_p \Phi^{(p)}, \qquad (2.5\text{-}07)$$

where the a_p are constants. This is the many-particle analogue of equation 2.4-05. In the exterior region,

$$\Psi = \frac{i}{2kr} \{ e^{-ikr} - S e^{ikr} \} \, \psi_{\mu 0} \, (\mathbf{n}) + \sum_{\mu \neq \mu_0} \psi_\mu(\mathbf{n}) \, A_\mu \frac{e^{ik_\mu r}}{r} \qquad (2.5\text{-}08)$$

(see equation 1.2-01), where the last term represents the outgoing waves for the possible inelastic scattering processes. A knowledge of the coefficients A_μ is not required for a calculation of the parameter S.

We can now proceed as in the previous section. The first problem is to calculate the coefficients a_p. Since the expansion 2.5-07 holds only in the interior region, we have, using the orthogonality condition 2.5-06,

$$\iint_0^R \{ \Phi^{(p)} H\Psi - \Psi H \Phi^{(p)} \} r^2 \, dr \, d\mathbf{n} = (E - W_p)a_p. \qquad (2.5\text{-}09)$$

By analogy with equations 2.4-13 and 2.4-14 we apply Green's theorem to the left-hand side of 2.5-09. The only components of H which contribute are the kinetic energy operators. Then

$$\iint_0^R \{ \Phi^{(p)} H_1\Psi - \Psi H_1 \Phi^{(p)} \} r^2 \, dr \, d\mathbf{n} = 0, \qquad (2.5\text{-}10)$$

provided that the eigenfunctions ψ_μ in the expansion 2.5-03 all obey the boundary condition $\psi_\mu = 0$ on the surface of the sphere. The remaining kinetic energy operator is H_2 . In configuration space this is

$$-\frac{1}{2M}\,\nabla^2,$$

where ∇ refers to the coordinate $\mathbf{r}$. Therefore, by Green's theorem and the expansion 2.5-03, the left-hand side of equation 2.5-09 equals

$$-\frac{1}{2M}\sum_{\mu,\lambda} a_{\mu\lambda}^p \int d\mathbf{n}\, R^2\, \psi_\mu(\mathbf{n}) \left\{\frac{\phi_{\mu\lambda}}{r}\nabla\Psi - \Psi\nabla\left(\frac{\phi_{\mu\lambda}}{r}\right)\right\}_{r=R}. \quad (2.5\text{-}11)$$

This equals

$$-\frac{1}{2M}\sum_{\mu,\lambda} a_{\mu\lambda}^p \int d\mathbf{n}\, \psi_\mu(\mathbf{n})\left\{\phi_{\mu\lambda}\frac{\partial(r\Psi)}{\partial r} - r\Psi\frac{\partial\phi_{\mu\lambda}}{\partial r}\right\}_{r=R}. \quad (2.5\text{-}12)$$

To evaluate the terms in the bracket, it is necessary to substitute equation 2.5-08 for $r\Psi$. The boundary condition 2.5-01 is then used to replace the derivative of $\phi_{\mu\lambda}$. It can then be seen that all terms containing the coefficients A_μ cancel. The integration over the variables $\mathbf{n}$ may be carried out using the orthogonality of the eigenfunctions ψ_μ . From the definition of k_μ (equation 2.5-02) and the chosen zero of energy, it is true that k_μ, for μ equal to μ_0 , is equal to k. The term 2.5-12 then equals

$$-\frac{1}{2M}\sum_\lambda a_{\mu0,\lambda}^p\, \phi_{\mu0,\lambda}(R)e^{-ikR}. \quad (2.5\text{-}13)$$

Combining this with equation 2.5-09, we have

$$a_p = -\frac{1}{2M}\cdot\frac{1}{E-W_p}\sum_\lambda a_{\mu0,\lambda}^p\, \phi_{\mu0,\lambda}(R)\, e^{-ikR}. \quad (2.5\text{-}14)$$

The parameter S may be calculated by equating the interior and exterior wave functions Ψ on the surface of the sphere. We have,

$$\Psi(R,\mathbf{n}) = \sum_p \sum_{\mu,\lambda} a_p a_{\mu\lambda}^p\, \psi_\mu\frac{\phi_{\mu\lambda}(R)}{R}. \quad (2.5\text{-}15)$$

Multiplying by $\psi_{\mu0}$ and integrating,

$$\int d\mathbf{n}\, \psi_{\mu0}\Psi(R, \mathbf{n}) = \sum_p \sum_\lambda a_p a_{\mu0,\lambda}^p \frac{\phi_{\mu0,\lambda}(R)}{R}. \quad (2.5\text{-}16)$$

For the exterior wave function 2.5-08,

$$\int d\mathbf{n}\, \psi_{\mu0}\Psi(R, \mathbf{n}) = \frac{i}{2kR}\{e^{-ikR} - Se^{ikR}\}. \quad (2.5\text{-}17)$$

Equating 2.5-16 and 2.5-17, and substituting for the a_p,

$$S = e^{-2ikR}\left\{1 - i\sum_p \frac{\gamma_p}{E - W_p}\right\}, \quad (2.5\text{-}18)$$

where the complex width γ_p is defined by

$$\gamma_p = \frac{k}{M}\sum_\lambda \sum_{\lambda'} a_{\mu0,\lambda}^p\, a_{\mu0,\lambda'}^p\, \phi_{\mu0,\lambda}(R)\, \phi_{\mu0,\lambda'}(R). \quad (2.5\text{-}19)$$

These equations are the many-particle analogues of equations 2.4-16 and 2.4-17. They represent the scattering amplitude in terms of the compound states $|\,p\rangle$.

Further discussion of these results will be given in the following section. The complete derivation, in which there is no restriction on angular momentum values, is contained in the paper of Brown (1959).

2.6 The Intermediate Model

The optical model of the nucleus makes the connection between the complex single-particle potential picture of equation 2.4-25 and the many-particle problem which leads to equation 2.5-18. The optical model is concerned with the averaged scattering parameter $\langle S_l \rangle$ introduced in Section 1.2. We shall relate the s-wave parameter $\langle S_0 \rangle$ of Section 1.2, to the parameters given by equations 2.4-25 and 2.5-18.

In Section 1.2, the idea of averaging functions of energy over an energy interval I was introduced. For the purposes of both the present section and Section 2.7, it will be convenient to give a definition of the averaging procedure. The function of energy it is required to average is the parameter $S(E)$ of equation 2.5-18. The compound state eigenvalues W_p have negative imaginary parts and S has simple analytic properties in the complex E plane. Apart from the branch point at the origin resulting from the momentum k, which is proportional to $\sqrt{E}$, there are a number of poles, given by $E = W_p$, lying in the complex plane below the real axis. For the arguments to be given, the $\sqrt{E}$ branch point can be neglected.

Consider a function $f(E)$ which is bounded at infinity and has the analytic properties outlined above. The average of the function over an interval I is

$$\langle f \rangle = \int_{-\infty}^{\infty} g(E - E')\, f(E')\, dE', \qquad (2.6\text{-}01)$$

where the weighting function is defined by

$$g = \frac{I}{\pi} \frac{1}{(E - E')^2 + I^2}. \qquad (2.6\text{-}02)$$

The weighting function has poles at $E' = E \pm iI$, and therefore 2.6-01 is obtained by integrating over the contour of Figure 1. The result is that

$$\langle f(E) \rangle = f(E + iI). \qquad (2.6\text{-}03)$$

It is now possible to introduce the optical model. We identify the complex potential $U - iW$ of Section 2.4 with

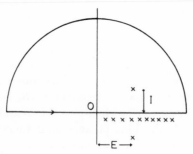

Fig. 1. Contour in the complex E' plane for the evaluation of the energy average of $S(E)$.

the optical model potential. Then the parameter S of equation 2.4–25 is to be identified with the $\langle S_0 \rangle$ of Section 1.2. Provided I is considerably smaller than the imaginary part of E_λ, application of the averaging procedure of equation 2.6-01 to equation 2.4-25 produces no change. This scattering parameter is from now onwards denoted by $\langle S \rangle \equiv \langle S_0 \rangle$. The compound elastic or fluctuation amplitude therefore depends on

$$S - \langle S \rangle = -ie^{-2ikR} \left\{ \sum_p \frac{\gamma_p}{E - W_p} - \sum_\lambda \frac{\Gamma_\lambda}{E - E_\lambda} \right\}, \quad (2.6\text{-}04)$$

where E_λ is the Kapur-Peierls eigenvalue for the complex single-particle potential. The average of this quantity must vanish. By equation 2.6-03,

$$\sum_p \frac{\gamma_p}{E + iI - W_p} = \sum_\lambda \frac{\Gamma_\lambda}{E - E_\lambda}. \quad (2.6\text{-}05)$$

The compound states are assumed to be long-lived so that the imaginary part of W_p is very much smaller than I.

In the intermediate model (Wigner, 1954; Scott, 1954; Lane, Thomas, and Wigner, 1955), when the energy of a compound state $|p\rangle$ is close to a given single-particle eigenvalue E_m, only the coefficients $a_{\mu\,m}^p$ are large and the other coefficients in the expansion of $\Phi^{(p)}$ (equation 2.5-03) for which $\lambda \neq m$ are all very small. Similarly, in the expansion 2.5-19 for the width γ_p of the compound state, only the coefficients $a_{\mu0,m}^p$ need be retained. Now the spacing between the s-state eigenvalues E_λ is very large, being typically of the order of 10 to 20 Mev. Therefore, I will be very much less than this spacing and the left-hand side of 2.6-05 will depend, through equation 2.5-19 for γ_p, only on the single-particle eigenstate m for which E_m coincides roughly with the interval I. An equivalent statement may be made by looking at the right-hand side of 2.6-05. From equation 2.4-24, the imaginary part of E_λ is roughly equal to $-W$. If W is very much smaller than the spacing between the s-state eigenvalues E_λ, then for $E \approx E_m$, the right-hand side depends on the eigenstate m only.

In the intermediate model, a compound state depends, through the expansion 2.5-03, only on the single-particle state to which it is very close. It does not depend on the other single-particle states. Such a simple statement cannot, however, be made for compound states which lie between single-particle states. These compound states must depend on two or more single-particle states λ, but both the coefficients $a_{\mu\lambda}^p$ and the widths γ_p will be small.

We can compare the intermediate model with the strong-coupling or compound model. In the strong-coupling case, all the coefficients would have to be retained in the expansions 2.5-03 and 2.5-19, and the left-hand side of equation 2.6-05 would depend on many single-particle states. The equivalent statement for the right-hand side of equation 2.6-05 is that the imaginary part of the optical model potential W, would be of the order of, or greater than the spacing between the single-particle states. For any given value of E, the right-hand side would then depend on many states λ. Such a very large value of W in the optical model would lead to the disappearance of the giant resonances and to monotonic behaviour of the total cross section as a function of energy, these being the predictions of the compound nucleus model. We shall show, later in this section, that the intermediate model is the correct one.

The intermediate model differs from the weak-coupling or shell model of the ground and low-lying excited states of nuclei in that the excitation energy of the compound nucleus is large, usually being at least 8 Mev. Whereas the ground and low-lying excited states of many nuclei may be constructed to a good approximation out of single-particle wave functions, the intermediate model does not suggest that the compound states $| p \rangle$ are of such elementary structure. Many states of the target contribute to a given compound state. Single-particle characteristics only become evident when the scattering amplitude is averaged over many compound states.

On the basis of the intermediate model, further results may be obtained from equation 2.6-05. They lead to the definition of the s-wave neutron strength function which is related to the energy-averaged total cross section. Let $\langle \gamma_p \rangle$ be the average of the γ_p in the interval I, and $1/D$ the average density of compound states. We consider an energy region in which the compound states are narrow and well spaced from each other. The energies W_p are nearly real, and the imaginary parts are very small compared with I. Then,

$$\text{Im} \sum_p \frac{\gamma_p}{E + iI - W_p} = -\frac{\bar{\gamma}I}{D} \int_{-\infty}^{\infty} \frac{dW_p}{(E - W_p)^2 + I^2},$$
$$(2.6\text{-}06)$$

where to a good approximation, W_p is taken to be a real variable. This approximation is correct if I includes many states $|p\rangle$. The quantity $\bar{\gamma}$ is the real part of $\langle \gamma_p \rangle$. By a simple contour integration,

$$- \text{Im} \sum_p \frac{\gamma_p}{E + iI - W_p} = \frac{\pi\bar{\gamma}}{D}, \qquad (2.6\text{-}07)$$

where the quantity on the right-hand side is known as the strength function. If the interval I is close to a given single-particle eigenstate m,

$$\frac{\pi\bar{\gamma}}{D} \approx - \text{Im} \left\{ \frac{\Gamma_m}{E - E_m} \right\}. \qquad (2.6\text{-}08)$$

Therefore, if $E \approx E_m$, the strength function has the Lorentz form.

The strength function is related to the part of the energy-averaged total cross section $\langle \sigma_t \rangle$, which is roughly proportional to $1/k$. If the energy is roughly equal to E_m and is such that kR is very small compared with unity, equation 2.4-25 gives

$$\text{Re} \langle S \rangle = 1 + \text{Im} \left\{ \frac{\Gamma_m}{E - E_m} \right\}$$

$$\approx 1 - \frac{\pi\bar{\gamma}}{D}. \qquad (2.6\text{-}09)$$

Therefore,

$$\langle \sigma_t \rangle = \frac{2\pi}{k^2} \left(1 - \text{Re} \langle S \rangle \right)$$

$$\approx \frac{2\pi}{k^2} \left(\frac{\pi \bar{\gamma}}{D} \right)$$

$$\approx \frac{2\pi}{k^2} \frac{\Gamma_m (W + w_m)}{(E - e_m)^2 + (W + w_m)^2}, \qquad (2.6\text{-}10)$$

since Γ_m is nearly real at low energy. The energy e_m is the real part of E_m. The energy-averaged total cross section therefore has giant resonances. For the Lorentz form given by equation 2.6-10 to be accurate, it is necessary that E should be both very small and close to the maximum of a giant resonance.

In order to make a comparison with experimental measurements of the strength function, a more complete formula for $\langle \sigma_t \rangle$ is required. In terms of the complex s-wave phase shift,

$$\delta = \delta_1 + i\delta_2, \qquad \langle S \rangle = e^{2i\delta}, \qquad (2.6\text{-}11)$$

and the averaged total cross section is

$$\langle \sigma_t \rangle = \frac{4\pi}{k^2} \{ \delta_2 + \delta_1^2 - \delta_2^2 \}, \qquad (2.6\text{-}12)$$

provided both parts of the phase shift are small. Near zero energy, the phase shift for scattering by an optical model potential is proportional to the momentum. Therefore, the first term in 2.6-12 is proportional to $1/k$ and the remaining terms, known as the potential scattering, are roughly constant. From equations 2.4-17 and 2.6-08, it can be seen that the strength function contribution to $\langle \sigma_t \rangle$ given by equation 2.6-10 is proportional to $1/k$. We may therefore identify the strength function with the imaginary part of the phase shift,

$$\frac{\pi \bar{\gamma}}{D} = + 2\delta_2. \qquad (2.6\text{-}13)$$

It is possible to remove the linear dependence on momentum of the strength function by defining

$$\frac{\bar{\gamma}^{(0)}}{D} = \left(\frac{E_0}{E}\right)^{\frac{1}{2}} \frac{\bar{\gamma}}{D}, \qquad (2.6\text{-}14)$$

where the reference energy E_0 is usually chosen to be 1 ev. The experimental measurements of $\bar{\gamma}/D$ are referred to the energy E_0 by equation 2.6-14. The theoretical values of $\bar{\gamma}^{(0)}/D$ are obtained by calculating δ_2 from the optical model potential. The comparison is made, as a function of mass number, in Figure 2, which is taken from the report of Campbell, Feshbach, Porter, and Weisskopf (1960). The solid curve is the theoretical prediction for an optical model potential of the Woods-Saxon form (equation 1.3-01). The parameters are

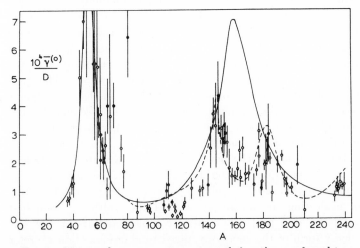

FIG. 2. Measured s-wave neutron strength functions, referred to an energy of 1 ev and multiplied by a factor of 10^4, are compared with the predictions of the optical models described in the text. The effect of increasing the imaginary central potential is to decrease the height of the giant resonances. (This Figure is from the Massachusetts Institute of Technology, Laboratory for Nuclear Science, Technical Report No. 73, 132, 1960. Researches described in this report were supported by the U.S. Atomic Energy Commission and the Office of Naval Research.)

$U = -52$ Mev, $W = 3.1$ Mev, $R = (1.15\,A^{1/3} + 0.4) \times 10^{-13}$ cm, and $a = 0.52 \times 10^{-13}$ cm. The experimental points are from the work of Hughes, Zimmerman, and Chrien (1958) and from a number of unpublished sources listed in the report of Campbell et al. The agreement is good in the region of the first giant resonance at $A = 55$ but is poor near $A = 150$. However, so far it has been assumed that the target nuclei are spherical, and it is known (see Temmer, 1958) that this is not true near $A = 150$. Deformation of the target nucleus and therefore of the optical model potential implies that the angular momentum of the incident nucleon is not a good quantum number. Therefore, angular momentum states are mixed, and in particular, the $l = 0$ giant resonance at $A = 151$ and the $l = 2$ giant resonance at $A = 147$ (Margolis, 1959). This leads to a splitting of the giant resonance predicted at $A = 151$ by the simple spherical nucleus theory. The broken curve in Figure 2 gives the values of $\bar{\gamma}^{(0)}/D$ calculated for a deformed trapezoidal optical model potential by Chase, Wilets, and Edmonds (1958). The curve is in good agreement with the experimental values, particularly near $A = 150$. This provides strong evidence for the intermediate model. The giant resonances in the strength function are not predicted by the strong-coupling model. References to earlier work are given in the review of Feshbach (1958b).

Investigation of the parts of 2.6-12 which are independent of k, the potential scattering terms, is not possible with the approximation used to obtain equation 2.6-10 which is one of neglecting the imaginary part of the width Γ_m compared with the real part. For more complete details of the low energy form of the energy-averaged total cross section we refer to the paper of Brown (1959).

The optical model of elastic scattering can be used to investigate giant resonance phenomena only for excitation energies, of the compound system, of about 8 Mev or more. Lower values of the excitation energy can be reached by study of nuclear rearrangement collisions such as the (d, p) reaction.

For further details of reactions of this kind see the review by Schiffer (1960).

A formulation of the optical model starting from the dispersion theory described in the last part of Section 2.4 has been given by Rosenfeld (1961). Complete surveys of the relation between nuclear dispersion theory and the optical model together with references to previous work are contained in the papers of Breit (1959) and of Brown (1959).

2.7 The Dispersion Formalism and the High Energy Expansion

In the previous sections, two completely different formulations of the optical model have been described. Section 2.2 showed how the optical model operator could be related through the cluster expansion 2.2-33 to the interactions between the incident particle and the separate nucleons in the target. However, arguments were presented in Section 2.3 to show that the cluster expansion is not uniformly convergent for some low energy regions. This difficulty is not a feature of the second formulation, which starts from a more suitable basic set of states, the compound states of the whole system. In this formulation, the relation between the optical model potential and the interactions between the incident and target nucleons is not so clear. We shall attempt to derive such a relation and use it to connect the high and low energy formulations.

In the derivation, it is necessary to introduce the transition amplitudes (equation 2.2-14) for the scattering by the target as a whole. At low energies, and for s-waves, we have

$$S = 1 - \frac{ikM}{\pi} \langle \mu_0, \mathbf{k}' \mid V \mid \Psi \rangle, \qquad (2.7\text{-}01)$$

and for the energy-averaged scattering parameter given by the optical model potential

$$\langle S \rangle = 1 - \frac{ikM}{\pi} \langle \mu_0, \mathbf{k}' \mid \mathbf{U} \mid \Phi \rangle, \qquad (2.7\text{-}02)$$

where $\langle S \rangle$ and S are given by equations 2.4-25 and 2.5-18. The scattering states $|\Psi\rangle$ and $|\Phi\rangle$ are defined by equations 2.2-04 and 2.2-08. If $(V - \mathbf{U})$ is taken to be the perturbation, that is

$$H = (H_1 + H_2 + \mathbf{U}) + (V - \mathbf{U}), \qquad (2.7\text{-}03)$$

the two states are connected by the equation

$$|\Psi\rangle = |\Phi\rangle + \frac{1}{E - H + i\epsilon} (V - \mathbf{U}) |\Phi\rangle. \qquad (2.7\text{-}04)$$

The difference between 2.7-01 and 2.7-02 is therefore

$$S - \langle S \rangle = -\frac{ikM}{\pi} \langle \mu_0, \mathbf{k}' | \left\{ V - \mathbf{U} \right.$$
$$\left. + V \frac{1}{E - H + i\epsilon} (V - \mathbf{U}) \right\} |\Phi\rangle. \qquad (2.7\text{-}05)$$

The left-hand side of equation 2.7-05 is proportional to the compound elastic or fluctuation amplitude, and therefore its energy average must vanish. By application of equation 2.6-03,

$$\mathbf{U} = V + V \frac{1}{E + iI - H} (V - \mathbf{U}), \qquad (2.7\text{-}06)$$

the representation being understood. From the rearrangement 2.7-03 we can carry out the formal expansion

$$(E + iI - H)^{-1} = \mathfrak{G} + \mathfrak{G}(V - \mathbf{U})\mathfrak{G} + \cdots, \qquad (2.7\text{-}07)$$

where

$$\mathfrak{G} = \mathfrak{G}(E + iI) = (E + iI - H_1 - H_2 - \mathbf{U})^{-1}. \qquad (2.7\text{-}08)$$

Therefore, we have

$$\mathbf{U} = V + V\mathfrak{G}(V - \mathbf{U}) + \cdots. \qquad (2.7\text{-}09)$$

Then equations 2.2-15 and 2.7-09 are identical except that the latter is to be evaluated at the complex energy $E + iI$.

The developments of Section 2.2 can be applied directly to equation 2.7-09, and we see that the dispersion formalism for the optical model is equivalent to the high energy formalism evaluated at the complex energy $E + iI$. However, this statement must be qualified by the possibility that the expansion 2.7-07 may not be permissible in some low energy regions unless I is very great, for the same reason that the series 2.2-33 fails to be uniformly convergent. Other perturbation schemes have been described by Brown, De Dominicis, and Langer (1959). For a convergent expansion, Brown (1959, 1960) found that I must be nearly as great as W.

2.8 The Nonlocality of the Potential

Practical applications of the optical model make use of the potential rather than the operator $\mathbf{U}$. The nonlocal properties of the potential are therefore of interest. The general form of the potential for finite target nuclei can be found from the high energy expansion 2.2-33. From equations 2.1-02, 2.1-08, and 2.1-12, we have, for a local and energy-independent nucleon-nucleon potential,

$$\langle \mu_0, \mathbf{k}' \mid \sum_i t_i + \cdots \mid \mu_0, \mathbf{k} \rangle$$

$$= \iint d\mathbf{r}' \, d\mathbf{r} \, e^{-i\mathbf{k}' \cdot \mathbf{r}'} \left\{ U(E, \mathbf{r}, \mathbf{r}') - iW(E, \mathbf{r}, \mathbf{r}') \right\} e^{i\mathbf{k} \cdot \mathbf{r}},$$

$$(2.8\text{-}01)$$

where $U - iW$ is the optical model potential and U and W are real functions of the variables indicated. The optical model potential is therefore both energy-dependent and nonlocal. The functions U and W which are the real and imaginary parts of the potential have different dependences on E and on $\mathbf{r} - \mathbf{r}'$. A complete investigation of the dependence of U, for bound nucleons, on $\mathbf{r} - \mathbf{r}'$ is contained in the paper of Brueckner, Gammel, and Weitzner (1958).

The nonlocality of the optical model potential for nuclei which may be thought of as infinite in extent is more restricted in form. The Schrödinger equation for a particle of mass M interacting through a nonlocal potential of infinite extent can be shown to be approximately equivalent to the equation for a particle of mass M^* interacting through a certain local potential. The mass M^* is known as the effective mass. The infinite nonlocal potential must be of the form

$$U(E, |\mathbf{r}' - \mathbf{r}|) - iW(E, |\mathbf{r}' - \mathbf{r}|), \quad (2.8\text{-}02)$$

where the dependence on $|\mathbf{r}' - \mathbf{r}|$ is a necessary consequence of the isotropy of infinite nuclear matter and of invariance under translations of the coordinate system. The Schrödinger equation for a particle of mass M and energy E interacting through a real infinite potential is therefore

$$-\frac{1}{2M} \nabla^2 \psi(\mathbf{r}) + \int d\mathbf{r}' \, U(E, |\mathbf{r}' - \mathbf{r}|) \psi(\mathbf{r}') = E\psi(\mathbf{r}).$$

$$(2.8\text{-}03)$$

A change of coordinate, $\mathbf{x} = \mathbf{r}' - \mathbf{r}$, leads to

$$\int d\mathbf{x} \, U(E, x) \psi(\mathbf{r} + \mathbf{x}) = \frac{1}{(2\pi)^3} \iint d\mathbf{x} \, d\mathbf{k} \, U(E, x) \psi(\mathbf{k}) \, e^{i\mathbf{k} \cdot (\mathbf{r} + \mathbf{x})},$$

$$(2.8\text{-}04)$$

where $\psi(\mathbf{k})$ is the Fourier transform of $\psi(\mathbf{r} + \mathbf{x})$. The angular integrations over $\mathbf{x}$ can now be carried out to give

$$\int d\mathbf{x} \, U(E, x) \, e^{i\mathbf{k} \cdot \mathbf{x}} = \frac{4\pi}{k} \int_0^\infty x \, dx \, U(E, x) \sin kx$$

$$= U^{(0)}(E) - \frac{k^2}{6} U^{(2)}(E) + \cdots \quad (2.8\text{-}05)$$

by an expansion of $\sin kx$ in powers of kx. The moments $U^{(n)}$ are defined by

$$U^{(n)}(E) = \int d\mathbf{x} \, x^n U(E, x). \quad (2.8\text{-}06)$$

Substituting 2.8-05 in 2.8-04, and with the result

$$\nabla^2 \int d\mathbf{k}\, \psi(\mathbf{k})\, e^{i\mathbf{k}\cdot\mathbf{r}} = -\int d\mathbf{k}\, k^2 \psi(\mathbf{k})\, e^{i\mathbf{k}\cdot\mathbf{r}}, \quad (2.8\text{-}07)$$

we have

$$\int d\mathbf{x}\, U(E, x)\, \psi(\mathbf{r} + \mathbf{x})$$

$$= U^{(0)}(E)\psi(\mathbf{r}) + \frac{1}{6}\, U^{(2)}(E)\nabla^2\psi(\mathbf{r}) + \cdots. \quad (2.8\text{-}08)$$

If we retain the first two terms only, the Schrödinger equation is

$$\left\{ -\frac{1}{2M} + \frac{1}{6}\, U^{(2)} \right\} \nabla^2\psi(\mathbf{r}) + U^{(0)}\psi(\mathbf{r}) = E\psi(\mathbf{r}). \quad (2.8\text{-}09)$$

The condition necessary for the second term of the series 2.8-08 to be much smaller than the first can be found by multiplying each term by $\psi^*(\mathbf{r})$ and integrating over $\mathbf{r}$. The condition is

$$\frac{U^{(2)} \int \psi^*\nabla^2\psi\, d\mathbf{r}}{U^{(0)} \int \psi^*\psi\, d\mathbf{r}} \ll 1, \quad (2.8\text{-}10)$$

which means that the product of the mean squared momentum of the nucleon and the square of the range of the nonlocality must be much smaller than unity. This condition, which is necessary for the equivalence of the nonlocal problem 2.8-03 and the local problem 2.8-09, can be satisfied only at very low kinetic energies. For example, if $U^{(2)}/U^{(0)} = 10^{-26}$ cm^2, then the ratio 2.8-10 is equal to $0.05\left(\dfrac{k^2}{2M}\right)$, where k^2 is the nucleon mean squared momentum.

The remaining problem, for infinite nuclear matter, lies in the dependence of the local potential in 2.8-09 on energy.

Multiplying 2.8-09 by $\psi^*(\mathbf{r})$ and integrating over $\mathbf{r}$, we have

$$\frac{k^2}{2M} + U(k^2) = E, \qquad (2.8\text{-}11)$$

where

$$U(k^2) = U^{(0)} - \tfrac{1}{6}k^2 U^{(2)}. \qquad (2.8\text{-}12)$$

With the Taylor expansion of the potential in powers of k^2,

$$U(k^2) = U(0) + k^2 \left\{\frac{\partial U}{\partial k^2}\right\}_{k^2=0} + \cdots, \qquad (2.8\text{-}13)$$

equation 2.8-11 becomes, keeping only terms in k^2,

$$\frac{k^2}{2M^*} + U(0) = E, \qquad (2.8\text{-}14)$$

where the effective mass is defined by

$$M^* = \frac{M}{1 + 2M \left\{\dfrac{\partial U}{\partial k^2}\right\}_{k^2=0}}. \qquad (2.8\text{-}15)$$

From 2.8-12, we have

$$\left\{\frac{\partial U}{\partial k^2}\right\}_{k^2=0} = \left\{\frac{\partial U^{(0)}}{\partial k^2}\right\}_{k^2=0} - \frac{1}{6} U^{(2)}(0), \qquad (2.8\text{-}16)$$

showing that the effective mass differs from the free mass M for two reasons. The first is the nonlocality which results in the term $U^{(2)}(0)$. The other term is caused by the energy dependence of the potential in 2.8-03.

The concept of an effective mass was first used in nuclear physics by Brueckner (1955), the purpose being to simplify the relation 2.8-11 between the energy and momentum of a nucleon moving in infinite nuclear matter. In Section 3.3 we shall show that the effective mass M^* is less than the free mass.

For a finite nucleus, provided the nonlocal potential is of the form $U(E, \mathbf{r}, x)$, the analysis from equation 2.8-03 to 2.8-09 is still good. The resulting equation

$$\left\{ -\frac{1}{2M} + \frac{1}{6} U^{(2)}(\mathbf{r}) \right\} \nabla^2 \psi + U^{(0)}(\mathbf{r})\psi = E\psi, \quad (2.8\text{-}17)$$

implies an effective mass which is a function of position. As $U^{(2)}(\mathbf{r})$ tends to zero in the nuclear surface, the effective mass tends to the free mass. The effective mass for a class of energy-independent, separable, nonlocal potentials has obtained by Frahn and Lemmer (1957). However, the series 2.8-08 is still usefully convergent only at very low energies, and for satisfactory calculation of the scattering of a nucleon by a finite nonlocal potential, it would appear to be necessary to obtain numerical solutions of the integro-differential equation 2.8-03.

CHAPTER 3

The Optical Model and Nuclear Structure

3.1 The Phenomenological Optical Model

In Section 2.6 we noted that at low energies the giant resonances in the s-wave neutron strength function[1] can be understood in terms of the optical model. The success of the intermediate model depends on the imaginary part of the optical model potential having a small value at low energies, and this is a consequence of the Pauli exclusion principle. The importance of the exclusion principle can be seen by considering the imaginary part of the optical model potential for negative K mesons. The imaginary part is large (about 50 Mev; see Section 3.5) at energies below 100 Mev, and is consistent with equation 1.1-05 if σ equals the free particle cross section.

At higher energies, the optical model can be used to determine the size and shape of the single-particle potential in which nucleons move. This problem will be described in Sections 3.1–3.3.

In Sections 3.1 and 3.3, the optical model will be taken to mean the replacement of the target nucleus by a local complex potential of the general form

$$V(\mathbf{r}) = V_c(r) + U_c b_1(r) - iW_c\{\zeta b_2(r) + (1 - \zeta)b_0(r)\}$$

$$+ \left(\frac{\hbar}{m_\pi c}\right)^2 \frac{1}{r}\left\{U_{s_0}\frac{db_3}{dr} - iW_{s_0}\frac{db_4}{dr}\right\}\mathbf{l}\cdot\mathbf{\sigma} \qquad (3.1\text{-}01)$$

where the Compton wavelength of the π-meson is a convenient

[1] The experimental p-wave strength function can also be fitted by the optical model (see Kreuger and Margolis, 1961).

scaling factor. l is the angular momentum of the incident nucleon and $(\frac{1}{2}\boldsymbol{\sigma})$ its spin operator. The form factor b_0 is gaussian,

$$b_0 = \exp\left\{-\left(\frac{r - R_0}{a_0}\right)^2\right\}. \qquad (3.1\text{-}02)$$

The remaining form factors are of the Woods-Saxon form,

$$b_i = \left\{1 + \exp\left(\frac{r - R_i}{a_i}\right)\right\}^{-1}, \qquad (3.1\text{-}03)$$

for $i = 1, 2, 3, 4$. The radial parameters are related to the mass number of the target by

$$R_0 = r_0 A^{1/3}, \quad R_i = r_i A^{1/3} + c_i. \qquad (3.1\text{-}04)$$

The general potential therefore has 19 adjustable parameters apart from the Coulomb potential. Special cases of this potential which have a smaller number of parameters have been used in all recent optical model analyses.

The Coulomb potential is usually chosen to be that given by a uniformly charged sphere of radius R_c,

$$V_c(r) = \frac{ZZ'e^2}{2R_c}\left(3 - \frac{r^2}{R_c^2}\right), \quad r < R_c$$

$$= \frac{ZZ'e^2}{r}, \quad r \geq R_c. \qquad (3.1\text{-}05)$$

This is a good representation of the Coulomb potential of a nuclear charge distribution with a diffuse surface (Woods and Saxon, 1954; Glassgold and Kellog, 1957). Some comparisons made by Buck, Maddison, and Hodgson (1960) show that a 5 % change in R_c alters the differential cross section for 17 Mev protons incident on Cu by about 1 % at backward scattering angles in the center of mass system. The polarisation at these angles, however, changes by about 4 %. The changes are smaller, for smaller values of θ.

The simple addition of the Coulomb potential to the nuclear

potential in 3.1-01 does not allow for Coulomb excitation of the target nucleus. There is no evidence that this process is important for proton scattering, but it could be important for heavy ions.

The inclusion of a potential which couples spin and orbital motion is necessary because nucleons elastically scattered from an unpolarised incident beam are observed to be polarised. A more complete discussion of the spin-orbit potential is given in the following section.

The target is assumed to be spherical and to have spin 0. Even though the nucleon-nucleon interaction is spin-dependent, this is thought to be a good approximation provided the target mass number is very much greater than the target spin, in units of $(\frac{1}{2}\hbar)$. An interaction which couples the incident nucleon and target spins would lead to many additional terms in the general potential 3.1-01. Numerical solution of the Schrödinger equation, including $V(\mathbf{r})$, may be carried out by the method outlined in Section 1.4 (for a more complete account, see Buck, Maddison, and Hodgson, 1960).

The potential 3.1-01 is an approximation to the true potential which represents the optical model operator $\mathbf{U}$. This simple form of the optical model may fail to fit the experimental cross sections for a number of reasons, most of which, at present, have not been completely investigated.

3.1.1 Nonlocality of the correct potential

It was established in Section 2.8 that the optical model potential is both nonlocal and energy dependent. The correct potential is a function of two configuration space coordinates and of the energy of the incident particle. However, the nonlocal potentials investigated by direct calculation have been separable functions of the form

$$V(\mathbf{r}, \mathbf{r}') = U(\tfrac{1}{2} | \mathbf{r} + \mathbf{r}' |)u(| \mathbf{r}' - \mathbf{r} |)$$
$$- iW(\tfrac{1}{2} | \mathbf{r} + \mathbf{r}' |)w(| \mathbf{r}' - \mathbf{r} |), \qquad (3.1\text{-}06)$$

where u and w are normalised and have volume integrals, over one coordinate, which are equal to unity. An angular distribution calculated for a potential of this class depends on the functions u and w, and an important problem is that the number of parameters in the potential is increased. For further discussion of this class of potentials we refer to Appendix A. Further problems which occur in the investigation of nonlocal optical model potentials are caused by the integro-differential equations which replace the partial wave equations 1.3-05.

3.1.2 *Nuclear deformation*

Many nuclei do not have spherical symmetry, but are deformed (see Temmer, 1958). The optical model potential should therefore include terms depending on the cosine of the angle (χ) between the axis of symmetry of the nucleus and the radius vector of the incident particle. The angular momentum of the incident particle would then not be a good quantum number. The importance of the deformation of target nuclei of mass number $A \approx 150$ has been shown, for slow neutrons, by the s-wave strength functions calculated by Chase, Wilets, and Edmonds (1958) and presented in Figure 2 of Section 2.6. The investigation of the effects of target deformation at higher energies is complicated by the mixing of angular momentum states. Recently, there has been interest in a generalized optical model for deformed nuclei, in which the potential includes a term which can cause transitions between the ground and first rotational states of the target. This extension of the model appears to give better estimates of the elastic scattering in those instances in which the first rotational state is strongly excited.

3.1.3 *Compound elastic scattering*

The optical model determines the shape elastic scattering (see Section 1.2) and not the measured elastic scattering cross section. The difference is the compound elastic scattering, which may be important for incident nucleon energies below about 10 Mev. The compound elastic scattering cross section is also the difference between the cross section for compound nucleus formation and the energy-averaged reaction cross section. The optical model potential which fits the elastic scattering at small momentum transfer can be used to calculate σ_c. The experimentally measured $\langle \sigma_r \rangle$ is then smaller than σ_c and the difference $\sigma_c - \langle \sigma_r \rangle$ is the compound elastic cross section σ_{ce}. Provided it is assumed that σ_{ce} is distributed as an isotropic differential cross section, it may be subtracted from the measured differential cross section to give the shape elastic scattering. Because the shape elastic scattering is mainly in the forward direction, the compound elastic scattering is most important for large values of θ. Some examples are given in the paper of Walt (1960). However, the difficulty in fitting the measured differential cross section with potentials extrapolated from higher energy analyses may also be the result of insufficient averaging over states of the compound nucleus.

3.1.4 *Averaging of the experimental cross sections*

Some examples in which the optical model parameters required to fit the neutron differential cross section vary rapidly with energy have been noted by Brown (1960) and by Walt (1960). For protons, similar examples are contained in the paper of Gugelot (1960). The most reasonable explanation is that one or more states of the compound nucleus are dominant and the experimental averaging is insufficient. Such a situation is most likely to occur for low values of the energy and mass number. For example, Rosen (1960) has shown that the experimental polarisation of 6 Mev elastically scattered protons varies irregularly with the target mass number A, for $A < 100$, but at 10.5 Mev, the variation is regular.[2]

3.1.5 *Exchange processes*

The simple optical model potential 3.1-01 does not take into account the identity of the incident and target nucleons. The

---

[2] For details of the fluctuations in W_c, at low energies and as a function of A, which can occur near closed shells, see Lane, Lynn, Melkonian, and Rae (1959) and Sugie (1960).

exchange process which is possible is a collision resulting in the incident nucleon taking the bound state of the target nucleon, while the target nucleon takes up a continuum state. The exchange causes substantial backward scattering which cannot be fitted by the simple optical model potential 3.1-01. This backward scattering can be described by an angular momentum dependent potential, for example, considering the real central part of 3.1-01,

$$2 U_c \rightarrow (U_c^+ + U_c^-) + (-1)^l (U_c^+ - U_c^-) \quad (3.1\text{-}07)$$

In the limit in which all odd-parity terms such as U_c^- vanish, only the even-l phase shifts are nonzero, and the angular distribution is symmetric about 90° in the many-body center of mass system. Therefore, a potential of the form 3.1-07 can give an increase in the scattering at backward angles. Such a potential was used by Gammel and Thaler (1958) to fit the angular distribution and polarisation of 20 to 40 Mev protons scattered by He⁴. In general, experimental angular distributions are such that exchange processes appear to be important only for small values of energy and target mass number.

3.1.6 *Spin-spin coupling*

The effect of coupling of the spin of the nucleon to the target spin is thought to be small provided the target mass number is very much greater than the spin, in units of $(\frac{1}{2}\hbar)$. An experimental test of this idea has been carried out by Rosen, Brolley, and Stewart (Rosen, 1960). It consists of comparing the polarisation of 10.5 Mev protons scattered by magnesium and aluminium. These nuclei are of nearly the same mass number but the spins are very different, being 0 for Mg^{24} and $\frac{5}{2}$ for Al^{27}. The comparison is made in Figure 3 as a function of the center of mass scattering angle θ. The polarisations are equal, within the limits of experimental accuracy, which is consistent with the idea that target spins are not important.

The problems outlined in Subsections 3.1.1, 3.1.3, 3.1.4, and 3.1.5 are most important for large values of the momentum

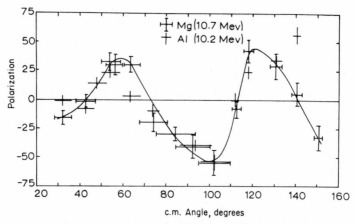

FIG. 3. The measured polarisations of protons scattered by Mg[24] and Al[27] are compared for a range of centre of mass angles (from Proc. of the International Conference on Nuclear Structure, Kingston, University of Toronto Press, 1960, p. 193).

transfer. Those outlined in Subsections 3.1.3, 3.1.4, 3.1.5, and 3.1.6 are important at energies less than about 10 Mev and also for low target mass numbers. We should not, as a consequence, expect the simple potential 3.1-01 to give a satisfactory prediction of the differential cross sections and polarisations for large values of the momentum transfer. In order to measure nuclear size by using the optical model, the incident nucleon should have an energy of about 10 Mev or greater.

3.2 Scattering and Polarisation of High Energy Nucleons

Measurements of the elastic scattering angular distribution and polarisation for high energy nucleons lead to both an understanding of the reaction mechanism and a determination of nuclear size. We begin this section with a brief description of the polarisation of a nucleon elastically scattered by a target of zero spin. The remainder of the section contains accounts of analyses based on either the impulse approximation or the phenomenological potential 3.1-01.

The scattering amplitude for the nucleon must be constructed from the vectors $\mathbf{k}$, $\mathbf{k}'$ and $\boldsymbol{\sigma}$, which are the initial and final momenta and the Pauli matrices. If the amplitude is to be invariant under the operations of rotation and space inversion, the most general form is

$$f = g(k, q) + h(k, q)\boldsymbol{\sigma} \cdot \mathbf{n}, \qquad (3.2\text{-}01)$$

where $\mathbf{q}$ is the momentum transfer and $\mathbf{n}$ is a unit axial vector perpendicular to the plane of scattering. The amplitude f is a 2×2 matrix, but g and h are functions as indicated. The determination of the polarisation P for the target, which we shall call the second target from now on, is made by measuring as a function of the azimuthal angle ω, the differential cross section for elastic scattering of an incident beam of known polarisation P'. The polarised beam is usually produced by scattering out from the first target which is placed in the internal beam of the accelerator. The plane of production is therefore known, and the polarisation P' is in a direction normal to this plane. The differential cross section for elastic scattering of this beam at the second target is

$$\frac{d\sigma}{d\Omega} = (|g|^2 + |h|^2)(1 + PP' \cos \omega), \qquad (3.2\text{-}02)$$

where $\cos \omega = \mathbf{n} \cdot \mathbf{n}'$ and $\mathbf{n}'$ and $\mathbf{n}$ are unit axial vectors normal to the plane of production at the first target and to the plane of scattering at the second target, respectively. The polarisation P for the second target is defined by

$$P = \frac{2Re\ (g^*h)}{|g|^2 + |h|^2}. \qquad (3.2\text{-}03)$$

P' depends on the mass number of the first target and on the angle of scattering at the first target, and is assumed to be known. The product PP' can be determined by measurement of the left to right asymmetry in 3.2-02, where the two directions are defined by $\mathbf{n}$ such that $\cos \omega = \pm 1$. The ratio of the differential cross sections for a fixed momentum transfer is

$$\frac{1 + PP'}{1 - PP'}. \tag{3.2-04}$$

The directions of the axial vectors **n** and **n**′ should be defined carefully for each individual experiment. A complete description of polarisation phenomena is contained in the paper of Wolfenstein (1956) (see also Hamilton, 1959, p. 375).

The polarisation P is the result of those components of the potential 3.1-01 which are proportional to $\mathbf{\sigma \cdot l}$. The derivative form of these parts of the potential was suggested by Fermi (1954) and is analogous to the Thomas spin-orbit potential for an electron interacting with a static Coulomb field,

$$\frac{1}{4m_e^2} \frac{1}{r} \frac{\partial}{\partial r} (V_c) \, \mathbf{\sigma \cdot l}, \qquad V_c = -\frac{Ze^2}{r} \tag{3.2-05}$$

(Hamilton, 1959, p. 128), where m_e is the mass of the electron. At high energies, and for light nuclei, the scattering of a nucleon by the optical model potential is given, to a good approximation, by the first term in the Born series 2.1-23. Under these conditions, it is possible to show that the second part of the amplitude 3.2-01 is given by the Thomas class of potentials in which V_c is replaced by a potential V of short range. We shall show this by calculating the Fourier transform

$$\frac{1}{4m^2} \int d\mathbf{r} \, e^{-i\mathbf{k'} \cdot \mathbf{r}} \left(\frac{1}{r} \frac{\partial V}{\partial r} \, \mathbf{\sigma \cdot l} \right) e^{i\mathbf{k} \cdot \mathbf{r}}, \tag{3.2-06}$$

where **k** and **k**′ are the initial and final momenta and $\mathbf{q} = \mathbf{k'} - \mathbf{k}$ is the momentum transfer. Because the initial state has a precise momentum **k**, we can make the replacement

$$\mathbf{\sigma \cdot l} \rightarrow \mathbf{\sigma \cdot (r \wedge k)} \tag{3.2-07}$$

and use the identity

$$i\mathbf{\sigma \cdot (r \wedge k)} = (\mathbf{\sigma \cdot r})(\mathbf{\sigma \cdot k}) - (\mathbf{r \cdot k}) \tag{3.2-08}$$

in order to carry out the angular integrations in 3.2-06. The exponential can be represented by a sum of products of two spherical harmonics,

$$e^{-i\mathbf{q}\cdot\mathbf{r}} = 4\pi \sum_l \sum_{m=-l}^{l} (-i)^l j_l(qr) Y_{lm}^*(\theta, \phi) Y_{lm}(\theta', \phi') \quad (3.2\text{-}09)$$

(Edmonds, 1957, p. 81), where $\mathbf{k}$ is chosen to be the fixed direction (z-axis). The angles θ and ϕ refer $\mathbf{r}$ to $\mathbf{k}$, and θ' and ϕ' refer $\mathbf{q}$ to $\mathbf{k}$. The function $j_l(qr)$ is a spherical Bessel function. By making the substitutions 3.2-08 and 3.2-09 and using the orthogonality of the spherical harmonics, the integral 3.2-06 equals

$$\frac{i}{4m^2} V(q)\mathbf{d}\cdot(\mathbf{k}' \wedge \mathbf{k}), \quad (3.2\text{-}11)$$

where $V(q)$ is the Fourier transform of $V(r)$. The unit axial vector in 3.2-01 is

$$\mathbf{n} = \frac{\mathbf{k}' \wedge \mathbf{k}}{kk' \sin \theta}, \quad (3.2\text{-}12)$$

where θ is the angle of scattering.

We can now see to what extent the elastic scattering and polarisation of high energy nucleons incident on light target nuclei are described by models based on the impulse approximation. From equation 2.3-09, the matrix element of the optical model operator is, for momentum transfer q and target mass number A,

$$\langle \mathbf{k}' \mid \mathbf{U} \mid \mathbf{k} \rangle = A\overline{\langle \mathbf{k}' \mid t_0 \mid \mathbf{k} \rangle}F(q), \quad (3.2\text{-}13)$$

where the form factor $F(q)$ is the Fourier transform of the nuclear density distribution,

$$F(q) = \int d\mathbf{r}\, \rho(r)\, e^{-i\mathbf{q}\cdot\mathbf{r}} \quad (3.2\text{-}14)$$

normalised in such a way that $F(0) = 1$. The transition operator t_0, in 3.2-13, describes the scattering of two free nucleons, and is an approximation to the operators t and τ, defined by equations 2.2-31 and 2.2-36, respectively, which describe the scattering of the incident nucleon by a bound nucleon in the target. The approximation of equation 2.3-03 is necessary for the derivation of 3.2-13. The nucleon-nucleon transition amplitude in 3.2-13 is assumed to depend only on the momentum of the incident nucleon in the many-body center of mass system and on the momentum transfer. No account is taken of the motion of the target nucleons. The nucleon-nucleon amplitude must be averaged, as indicated in 3.2-13, over the spins and isotopic spins of the target nucleons.

At very high energies, the impulse approximation is good because the kinetic energy of the target nucleon is very much smaller than any other energy involved in evaluating the intermediate states in the series 2.2-31 or 2.2-36. However, the approximation of neglecting higher terms in the cluster expansion 2.2-33 must rely on agreement with experimental results for its justification. Evidence of good agreement with experiment for low values of the momentum transfer will be presented later in this section.

From equation 2.1-23, the Born approximation scattering amplitude in the many-particle center of mass system is

$$f_B = -\frac{A^2 m}{(A+1)2\pi} \overline{\langle \mathbf{k}' \mid t_0 \mid \mathbf{k} \rangle} F(q), \qquad (3.2\text{-}15)$$

where m is the mass of the nucleon. It should be noted, however, that equation 2.1-23 is nonrelativistic.

The free nucleon-nucleon scattering amplitude in the two-particle center of mass system is of the form

$$A + B(\mathbf{\sigma}_1 \cdot \mathbf{n})(\mathbf{\sigma}_2 \cdot \mathbf{n}) + C(\mathbf{\sigma}_1 \cdot \mathbf{n} + \mathbf{\sigma}_2 \cdot \mathbf{n})$$

$$+ \frac{E}{q^2} (\mathbf{\sigma}_1 \cdot \mathbf{q})(\mathbf{\sigma}_2 \cdot \mathbf{q}) + F(\mathbf{\sigma}_1 \cdot \mathbf{p})(\mathbf{\sigma}_2 \cdot \mathbf{p}), \quad (3.2\text{-}16)$$

where $\mathbf{\sigma}_1$ and $\mathbf{\sigma}_2$ are the spin operators for the two nucleons and $\mathbf{n}$ is a unit axial vector perpendicular to the scattering plane. The vector $\mathbf{p}$ is a unit polar vector defined by

$$\mathbf{p} = (\mathbf{q} \wedge \mathbf{n}) \mid \mathbf{q} \wedge \mathbf{n} \mid^{-1}, \qquad (3.2\text{-}17)$$

and A, B, C, E, and F are functions of k and q and of the isotopic spin. This form is given, for example, in the paper of

Kerman, McManus, and Thaler (1959). For an even-even target nucleus having equal numbers of neutrons and protons and zero spin and isotopic spin, we have, from equation 2.1-23,

$$-\frac{m}{4\pi} \overline{\langle \mathbf{k'} \mid t_0 \mid \mathbf{k} \rangle} = \bar{A} + \bar{C}\boldsymbol{\sigma} \cdot \mathbf{n}, \qquad (3.2\text{-}18)$$

where

$$\bar{A} = \tfrac{3}{4}A_1 + \tfrac{1}{4}A_0 ,$$
$$\bar{C} = \tfrac{3}{4}C_1 + \tfrac{1}{4}C_0 , \qquad (3.2\text{-}19)$$

the subscripts denoting the isotopic spin. For such a target nucleus, the remaining terms in 3.2-16 all become zero when the average over target nucleon spins is formed. Values of $\bar{A}$ and $\bar{C}$ calculated from the phenomenological potentials of Gammel and Thaler (1957), are tabulated for a range of values of energy and momentum transfer in the paper of Kerman et al.

The Born approximation amplitude in the many-particle center of mass system is therefore

$$f_B = \frac{2A^2}{A+1} F(q)(\bar{A} + \bar{C}\boldsymbol{\sigma} \cdot \mathbf{n}), \qquad (3.2\text{-}20)$$

which is the same as equation 4.9 of Kerman et al. This amplitude has the necessary general form 3.2-01.

From 3.2-03, the polarisation is

$$P = \frac{2 \operatorname{Re} (\bar{A}^* \bar{C})}{\mid \bar{A} \mid^2 + \mid \bar{C} \mid^2}, \qquad (3.2\text{-}21)$$

which is independent of the target form factor. The amplitude $\bar{C}$ is strongly dependent, for small momentum transfer, on the momentum in the two-particle center of mass system. Because of the approximation 2.3-03 which has been used to derive 3.2-20 and 3.2-21, this momentum is equal (nonrelativistically) to half the momentum of the incident nucleon in the laboratory system and is independent of the target mass number. Therefore, in the laboratory system, the polarisation 3.2-21 is independent of the target mass number.

The total amplitude 3.2-20 is equal to the sum of the amplitudes for scattering by the individual nucleons in the target. This approximation is fair for high energies and small momentum transfers.

The formulae 3.2-20 and 3.2-21 have been compared, by many authors, with the experimental differential cross sections and polarisations for fast nucleons. The procedure is to calculate $\bar{A}$ and $\bar{C}$ from a given set of nucleon-nucleon phase shifts, or from a phenomenological nucleon-nucleon potential. The form factor $F(q)$ is calculated from the nuclear density distribution given by the differential cross section for high energy electron scattering (Hofstadter, 1957). Bethe (1958) started from the potential of Gammel and Thaler (1957) and the sets of phase shifts for 310 Mev proton-proton scattering found by Stapp, Ypsilantis, and Metropolis (1957). The comparison was made for the scattering of 310 Mev protons by carbon, and both the angular distribution calculated from 3.2-20, and the polarisation, were found to be in substantial agreement with the experimental values. Similar comparisons have been made by McManus and Thaler (1958) and by Wilson (1959) for nucleon energies in the range 90 to 310 Mev.

The dependence of $\bar{A}$ on q means that the central optical model potential has a greater radial extent than the nuclear density distribution. We can see this by forming the Fourier transform of 3.2-13. From equations 3.2-13 and 3.2-18, we have the momentum dependent optical model potential

$$V(k, \mathbf{r}) = -\frac{2A}{(2\pi)^2 m} \int d\mathbf{q}\, F(q)(\bar{A} + \bar{C}\boldsymbol{\sigma}\cdot\mathbf{n})\, e^{i\mathbf{q}\cdot\mathbf{r}}. \quad (3.2\text{-}22)$$

The central potential form factors will be equal to the form factor of the nuclear density distribution only if $\bar{A}$ is independent of q, which would be true if the nucleon-nucleon force were of zero range. Equation 3.2-22 implies that the parameter ζ in 3.1-01 is very nearly unity at high energies; there is no concentration of absorption at the surface of the nucleus. A further point is that if the real and imaginary parts of $\bar{A}$ are different functions of q, the real and imaginary parts of the central optical model potential will have different radii. This was noted by all the above authors. The nucleon-nucleon phase shifts used imply that the real part of the potential has a greater radius than the imaginary part. At present, there is no other evidence for such a difference. However, the potential is required to have a greater radius than the density distribution in order to fit the experimental angular distribution in the forward direction.

The spin-orbit part of the potential 3.2-22 depends on $\bar{C}$. The sets of phase shifts result in a complex function $\bar{C}$, and therefore the impulse approximation model predicts that the spin-orbit potential should have both real and imaginary parts.

The need, at high energies, for a complex spin-orbit part in the phenomenological potential 3.1-01 was shown by Heckrotte (1956). It is necessary in order to account for the variation of the polarisation with scattering angle. In this respect, the impulse approximation model is accordant with the phenomenological optical model.

The spin-orbit potential decreases with energy. For example, at 310 Mev, Bethe (1958) found U_{s_0} to be about one fifth of the value required by the nuclear shell model. The signs of the potential and of the polarisation at high energies cannot be found from the experimental left-right asymmetry because this determines only the product PP'. An interference effect is required. Schwinger (1948) showed that the Coulomb spin-orbit potential for neutrons resulting from the anomalous magnetic moment could produce a measurable contribution to the polarisation at small angles. It is known that the Born approximation gives a good description of the polarisation at high energies and small angles (Köhler, 1956) so that the amplitude h in 3.2-01 is well represented by the sum of the Born amplitudes for the Coulomb and nuclear spin-orbit potentials. This gives the required interference effect. In this way, Heckrotte (1956) and Voss and Wilson (1956) were able to show that U_{s_0} in 3.1-01 is positive.

The elastic scattering and polarisation may be calculated by exact solution of the Schrödinger equation including the potential 3.2-22 derived by the impulse approximation. This will then include the multiple scattering processes shown in equation 2.3-34, and the resulting differential cross section and polarisation will be better approximations than 3.2-20 and 3.2-21. Calculations of this kind have been carried out by Cromer (1959), Kerman, McManus, and Thaler (1959), and by Johansson, Svanberg, and Hodgson (1961). The predictions are in good agreement with experiment. This is illustrated by Figures 4, 5, and 6 which are taken from the paper of Johansson et al., and refer to the scattering of 180 Mev protons. The polarisations of protons scattered by lithium and by carbon are shown in Figures 4 and 5. Johansson et al. start from the development of Kerman et al. which is described in Section 2.2. In this development, the predicted potential is equal to 3.2-22 with the target mass number A replaced by A-1. The differential cross section calculated by solution of the Schrödinger equation must then be multiplied by a factor $\{A/(A-1)\}^2$. The calculated polarisation is the correct one. This polarisation, represented by the broken lines in Figures 4 and 5, is in good agreement with the experimental points. For center of mass scattering angles less than 20°, the experimental polarisations for lithium and carbon are very nearly the same, as is predicted by the Born approximation result 3.2-21. Figure 6 shows the differential cross section for carbon.

Some phenomenological analyses have been carried out at high energies, and we refer to the papers of Johansson et al. and of Hodgson (1961a) for further details. The main problem at high energies is that very large values of the momentum transfer are possible and the effects of the nonlocality of the correct potential should be investigated.

The main results of this section can be summarised by two statements. Firstly, the reaction mechanism at high energies is well described by the impulse approximation. Secondly, the form factor of the nuclear density distribution derived from

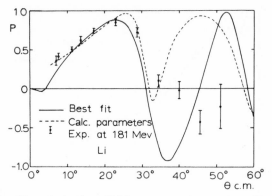

FIG. 4. The polarisation of high-energy protons scattered by lithium is compared with the prediction, given by the broken curve, of the optical model discussed in the text. The solid curve shows the polarisation calculated from a best-fit phenomenological potential. For further details see the paper of Johansson *et al.* (from Arkiv för Fysik, Band 19 nr 39, 560; Almqvist and Wiksell, Stockholm, 1961).

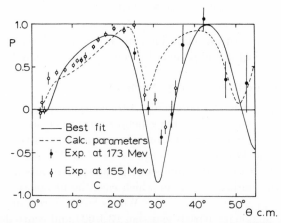

FIG. 5. The polarisation of high-energy protons scattered by carbon. Johansson *et al.*, corrected for the energy differences between the measured points and the curves (from Arkiv för Fysik, Band 19 nr 39, 562, 1961).

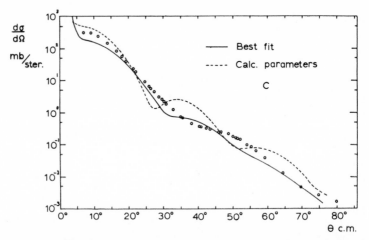

FIG. 6. The differential cross section for the scattering of 180 Mev protons by carbon. The broken curve gives the prediction of the optical model discussed in the text, and the solid curve, the differential cross section calculated from a best-fit phenomenological potential (from Arkiv för Fysik, Band 19 nr 39, 562, 1961).

high energy electron scattering can be used to calculate a satisfactory optical model potential through the relation 3.2-22.

3.3 Intermediate Energy Nucleons

The optical model potential 3.1-01 contains nineteen adjustable parameters and is of too general a form to be used in fitting experimental data. For example, many authors have assumed that all the Woods-Saxon form factors (3.1-03) are equal. A further decrease in the number of parameters results if it is assumed that either $\zeta = 1$, in which case the imaginary part of the central potential is of the Woods-Saxon form, or $\zeta = 0$ and the imaginary part is gaussian (3.1-02) and centred at the nuclear surface. These two possibilities will be referred to as volume and surface absorption respectively.

The need for smoothly varying form factors was conclusively shown by Woods and Saxon (1954). This can be seen, in outline, by observing that a square well potential surface reflects more of the incident wave than a Woods-Saxon surface. A square well optical model potential therefore predicts too small a reaction cross section, and too great a differential elastic scattering cross section at large angles. The spin-orbit potential gives the polarisation of the scattered nucleon, and in addition smooths out the maxima and minima in the calculated differential cross section at backward angles (Bjorklund and Fernbach, 1958), a result which in general much improves agreement with the experimental angular distributions. More complete details and some examples of the effects of varying parameters of the potential are given in the paper of Melkanoff, Nodvik, Saxon, and Woods (1957).

The most obvious measure of nuclear size is the radial parameter R_1 for the real part of the central potential. The parameters of the potential 3.1-01 determined in three recent analyses are shown in Table 1. The first line shows the surface absorption potential determined by Bjorklund and Fernbach (1958) for 14 Mev neutrons. The experimental data used were the differential, reaction, and total cross sections. The experimental values of the reaction and total cross sections are compared in Figure 7 with those calculated from this best-fit potential for a number of values of $A^{1/3}$. The agreement is excellent. The second line shows the best-fit volume absorption potential determined by Rosen, Brolley, and Stewart (1961) (see also Rosen, 1960) from the elastic scattering of polarised 10 Mev protons by a large number of elements. The third line shows the best-fit volume absorption potential determined by Nodvik and Saxon (1960) from the differential cross section and polarisation of 10 Mev protons scattered by argon and copper. The result of each analysis is a potential radius greater than the charge radius measured by high energy electron scattering ($r_1 = 1.07 \times 10^{-13}$ cm and $a_1 = 0.55 \times 10^{-13}$ cm; Hofstadter, 1957).

There are two reasons for such a difference (Berg and Wilets, 1956; Brueckner, 1956). The first is the finite range of the nucleon-nucleon potential. The second reason is the nonlinear

Table 1

	E	ζ	U_c	W_c	r_1	a_1	r_0	a_0	U_{s_0}	W_{s_0}
BF (neutron)	14	0	−44	11	1.25	0.65	1.25	0.98	8.3	0
RBS (proton)	10	1	−55	6	1.2	0.5	—	—	7.0	0
NS (proton)	10	1	−55	8	1.26	0.52	—	—	3.5	1.0
RML (neutron)	—	1	−43	0	1.30	0.69	—	—	9.4	0
(proton)	—	1	−54	0	1.30	0.69	—	—	9.4	0

The first three lines of the table show the parameters of the best-fit optical model potentials determined by Bjorklund and Fernbach (1958), Rosen, Brolley and Stewart (1961), and Nodvik and Saxon (1960). For each potential, the constants c_i (3.1-04) are zero and the Woods-Saxon form factors (3.1-03) are equal. The fourth and fifth lines show the potentials for bound neutrons and protons determined by Ross, Mark, and Lawson (1956). Energies are in Mev and the unit of length is 10^{-13} cm. The parameters are defined in Section 3.1.

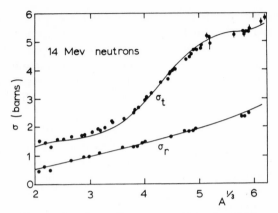

F[IG]. 7. The total and reaction cross sections for 14 Mev neutrons calculated from the best-fit surface absorption potential of Table 1 are compared, as functions of $A^{1/3}$, with the experimental cross sections (adapted from Phys. Rev. **109**, 1298, 1958).

variation of the nucleon-nucleus potential with nuclear density ρ, a condition necessary for saturation. If $\bar{U}_c$ and $\bar{K}$ are the average potential and kinetic energies, the equilibrium condition is

$$\frac{\partial \bar{U}_c}{\partial \rho} = -\frac{\partial \bar{K}}{\partial \rho}.$$

In a large nucleus, the average kinetic energy of a nucleon is approximately proportional to $\rho^{2/3}$ (Blatt and Weisskopf, 1952, p. 122). In the neighbourhood of the equilibrium density, $\bar{U}_c$ must therefore be proportional to a lesser power of ρ. The idea that nuclear matter in the surface region has, in this respect, the same properties as nuclear matter in the interior, results in the potential having a greater radial extent than the density distribution. Brueckner (1956) estimated the difference resulting from the saturation of nuclear forces to be about 0.5×10^{-13} cm for a heavy nucleus. The sum of the saturation and finite-range increases is sufficient to account for the observed difference of about 10^{-13} cm.

The most complete determination of U_c as a function of energy is that of Bowen, Scanlon, Stafford, Thresher, and Hodgson (1961). They measured the neutron total cross sections for carbon, aluminium, copper, cadmium, lead, and uranium, in the energy range 15 to 120 Mev. These total cross sections have broad maxima, for example, at about 20 and 80 Mev, for lead. The positions depend on the nuclear radius and on the wave number of the incident neutron inside the nucleus, which is determined by the energy and the real central potential. Bowen et al. chose $r_1 = 1.25 \times 10^{-13}$ cm and found the real central potentials which fit the positions and shapes of the maxima. For further details we refer to their paper. The potentials are shown in Figure 8. The real central part becomes less negative with increasing energy, and the effective nucleon mass at the center of the nucleus, determined from Figure 8 and equations 2.8-11 and 2.8-14, is $M^* = 0.75\ M$.

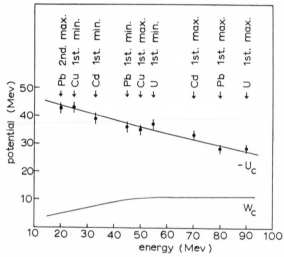

FIG. 8. The nine points are determinations, at different energies, of the real central part of the optical model potential for neutrons, by the method of Bowen et al. described in the text. The curve is fitted to the points (from Nuclear Phys. **22,** 659; North-Holland Publishing Co., Amsterdam, 1961).

There are several problems in determining a unique potential which gives the best fit to a given set of experimental data. First of all, it is necessary to decide how the data are to be used. Let x_i be an experimental measurement of an observable having an error Δx_i, and x_i' the value calculated from the optical model potential. Then the most simple fitting procedure is one of finding the potential parameters which minimise the quantity

$$\sum_i \left(\frac{x_i' - x_i}{\Delta x_i} \right)^2. \tag{3.3-01}$$

However, this assumes that the optical model is capable of fitting, for example, the large momentum transfer points in an angular distribution, whereas the ideas put forward in Section 3.1 indicate that the model is expected to be accurate only at small momentum transfers. It is therefore a reasonable first requirement that the small momentum transfer results be fitted by the potential. The potential which minimises 3.3-01 may not satisfy this requirement, and 3.3-01 should, in principle, be replaced by a form giving greater weight to a correct fitting of low momentum transfer data.

Minimising a quantity such as 3.3-01 for an elastic scattering angular distribution does not determine a unique potential, but only the product $U_c R_1^n$, where $2 < n < 3$. This ambiguity has been noted by many authors, and for example, Nodvik and Saxon (1960) find that $n \approx 2.3$ for 10 Mev protons scattered by argon and copper.

Seth, Hughes, Zimmerman, and Garth (1958) and Seth (1958) have shown how the ambiguity can be resolved by measurement, as a function of mass number, of the s-wave potential scattering cross section for slow neutrons. The potential scattering amplitude is that part of the low energy neutron scattering amplitude which is approximately independent of momentum. As a function of mass number it has resonances at the same values of A as the s-wave strength function. Seth et al. have compared the experimental potential scattering cross section with the predictions of a central optical model potential and find $r_1 = 1.35 \times 10^{-13}$ cm, $a_1 = 0.58 \times 10^{-13}$ cm, $U_c =$

-42 Mev, and $W_c = 3.4$ Mev, showing that the radius of the potential is greater than the radius of the charge distribution. As in the case of the strength function, it is found that a distorted (nonspherical) potential leads to improved agreement near $A = 150$.

The possibility of a volume absorption potential in which the form factors of the real and imaginary central parts are different has at present, owing to the increased number of parameters, received little consideration. The optical model potential predicted by the impulse approximation (equation 3.2-22) at high nucleon energies does have different form factors, and such differences may be expected to exist at lower energies.

The difference between the real and imaginary central parts is more extreme in the surface absorption model, the imaginary part of the potential having a maximum at the nuclear surface. Such a possibility is allowed for by the parameter ζ in 3.1-01. Existing analyses consider only the limiting cases $\zeta = 0$ or 1. We shall first consider the results of these analyses and then go on to describe briefly the theoretical points of view.

The starting point is the idea that for a given energy, the optical model potentials required to fit, for example, neutron reaction and differential elastic scattering cross sections, should not vary with mass number to any considerable extent. Bjorklund (1959) and Walt (1960), for neutrons of 10 to 20 Mev, have noted that in the volume absorption potential, W_c must decrease by as much as a factor of two in going from light to heavy nuclei. Such a variation does not occur in the surface absorption model.

Further information can be obtained if the experimental data are complete, that is, the reaction cross section, differential elastic scattering cross section, and polarisation are all known. Such complete data exist for protons of about 9.5 Mev. The most difficult quantity to measure is the reaction cross section. This has been measured in two ways. Greenlees and Jarvis (1960) measured the reaction cross section for copper at a proton energy of 9.3 Mev, by an attenuation method. The other method, used by Meyer and Hintz (1960) and by Albert and Hansen (1961), consists of separately measuring the cross section for each inelastic channel. The reaction cross section, which is the sum over all inelastic channels, is in good agreement with the measurement of Greenlees and Jarvis. The reaction cross sections predicted by the surface and volume absorption potentials which fit the polarisation and elastic scattering are compared with the experimental cross sections in Figure 9, which is taken from the paper of Albert and Hansen. The conclusion is that the surface absorption model is favoured. However, Meyer and Hintz have pointed out that the correct reaction cross sections would probably result from a volume absorption potential in which the imaginary central part ex-

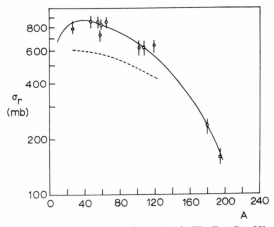

Fig. 9. The reaction cross sections of Al, Ti, Fe, Co, Ni, Cu[63, 65], Rh, AG, Sn, Ta, and Au for protons of about 9.5 Mev, measured by Meyer and Hintz and by Albert and Hansen, are compared with the predictions of volume and surface absorption optical models. The broken curve is predicted by the volume absorption potential given in the third line of Table 1. The solid curve is the prediction of a surface absorption potential having $U_c = -(44 + Z/A^{1/3})$, $W_c = 11$, $r_0 = r_1 = 1.25$, $a_1 = 0.65$, $a_0 = 1.2$, in units of Mev and of 10^{-13} cm, and a spin-orbit potential equal to the Thomas potential (3.3-04) multiplied by a factor of -20 (from Phys. Rev. **123**, 1750, 1961).

tends further than the real part. This conjecture requires further investigation.

A number of authors have calculated the radial dependence of the imaginary part of the potential using the Thomas-Fermi approximation. This approximation assumes that a Fermi energy can be defined as a function of the nucleon density and therefore of radial position, and which is equal to the Fermi energy of an infinite system having the same density. The Fermi energy equals

$$\frac{1}{2m} \left(\frac{3}{2} \pi^2 \rho \right)^{2/3} , \qquad (3.3\text{-}02)$$

where m is the mass of the nucleon, and the numbers of neutrons and protons are assumed to be equal.

The imaginary part of the potential is given, to a first approximation, by forming the Fourier transform of equation 2.3-01 and calculating the interaction between the incident and target nucleons by second order perturbation theory. Thus,

$$W(r) = -\frac{A}{(2\pi)^3} \, \text{Im} \int d\mathbf{q} \, \langle \mu_0, \mathbf{k}' \mid v \alpha G(E) v \mid \mu_0, \mathbf{k} \rangle e^{i(\mathbf{k}'-\mathbf{k}) \cdot \mathbf{r}}$$

$$(3.3\text{-}03)$$

with the notation of Section 2.2. This function can be evaluated for an infinite Fermi gas to give W as a function of the density. The imaginary part of the potential at a known radial position and therefore nucleon density is then, in this model, equal to the imaginary part for the infinite Fermi gas of the same density. Owing to the Pauli exclusion principle, both the incident and the target nucleons in the intermediate state in 3.3-03 must have momenta greater than the Fermi momentum of the infinite gas. The exclusion principle, at low energies, results in the imaginary part calculated from 3.3-03 being an order of magnitude less than that given by 1.1-05. Moreover, owing to the exclusion principle, the imaginary part is not proportional to the nucleon density as in 1.1-05 but decreases more slowly. The model predicts that the imaginary part of the potential will have a maximum at the nuclear surface. As the energy is increased, and the exclusion principle becomes less important, the maximum at the surface should disappear. These ideas are contained in the papers of Gomes (1959), Harada and Oda (1959), Kikuchi (1959), Shaw (1959), and Sawicki and Moszkowski (1960).

Lemmer, Maris, and Tang (1959) and Jancovici (1960) did not make the Thomas-Fermi approximation. They evaluated 3.3-03 by using an explicit set of single-particle wave functions for a finite nucleus and also found the imaginary part of the potential to have a maximum at the nuclear surface. The imaginary part of the potential at the centre of the nucleus is finite, and the ratio of the maximum potential to the potential at the centre is large at very low energies but tends to unity at high energies.

The single-particle potentials for bound neutrons and protons which lead to the observed shell structure and to the correct separation energy for the last nucleon, have been determined by Ross, Mark, and Lawson (1956). The parameters of the potentials are shown in the last two lines of Table 1. The neutron potential shown in the table gives $3s$ and $4s$ giant resonances in the total cross section at $A = 56$ and 166, respectively. The spin-orbit potential is equal to the Thomas potential defined for a neutron,

$$\frac{1}{4m^2} \frac{U_c}{r} \frac{\partial b_1}{\partial r} \, \mathbf{\sigma} \cdot \mathbf{l} \qquad (3.3\text{-}04)$$

multiplied by a factor of -40.

Table 1 shows that the spin-orbit potentials found in the three optical model analyses are of the same sign and magnitude as the spin-orbit potential determined from the nuclear shell model. The values of the real central optical model potentials are very nearly equal to the shell model potentials, but the radial parameters of the shell model potentials are a little greater.

The optical model potentials of Table 1 show the existence of a symmetry term, which is the difference of 11 Mev between the neutron and proton real central potentials. There are two reasons for this difference (Lane, 1957; Moszkowski, 1957; Green and Sood, 1958; Satchler, 1958). The first is the momentum dependence of the potential. For the same total energy, protons have a smaller kinetic energy than neutrons owing to the Coulomb potential, and therefore experience a more attractive nuclear potential. Secondly, the number of protons (Z) in the target is less than the number of neutrons (N). The strongest attractive nucleon-nucleon interaction is in the triplet s-state, which is forbidden for like pairs (n-n and p-p) by the Pauli exclusion principle. Because an incident proton can form more unlike pairs than an incident neutron, the proton potential should be more attractive. Moszkowski and Satchler estimate that the symmetry term (also known as the proton potential anomaly) should be of the order of

$$45 \left(\frac{N - Z}{A} \right) \text{Mev}, \qquad (3.3\text{-}05)$$

which is a little less than the potential differences shown in Table 1.[3]

The variation of the optical model potential with energy can be found by comparing the best-fit potentials of Table 1 with, for example, the best-fit potentials found by Johansson, Svan-

---

[3] A. M. Lane (1962) has pointed out that the optical model potential should be dependent on isotopic spin, the real central part being of the form,

$$U_c + \frac{\Delta U_c}{A} \, \mathbf{t} \cdot \mathbf{T},$$

where $\mathbf{t}$ and $\mathbf{T}$ are the isotopic spins of the nucleon and target, respectively. The difference between the neutron and proton potentials,

$$\frac{1}{2} \left(\frac{N - Z}{A} \right) \Delta U_c,$$

is to be identified with 3.3-05. Lane concludes that the best determination of ΔU_c can be made by an optical model fit of the cross section for charge exchange scattering of protons where the final nucleus is a member of the same isotopic spin multiplet as the initial target nucleus.

berg, and Hodgson (1961) at 180 Mev. Johansson et al. found
$U_c \approx -16$ Mev and $U_{s_0} \approx 2.5$ Mev, showing that both the
central and spin-orbit real parts decrease with energy. The real
central part decreases to nearly zero at 310 Mev (see Bethe,
1958; Kerman, McManus, and Thaler, 1959). There is some
evidence that the central imaginary part increases slowly with
energy for the surface absorption model. For example, Bjorklund and Fernbach (1958) found $W_c = 7$, 9.5 and 11 Mev for
neutron energies of 4.1, 7 and 14 Mev, respectively. However,
the values of the spin-orbit imaginary part are not well determined at any energy.

3.4 Compound Particles and the Nuclear Surface

In some recent experiments, measurements have been made
of angular distributions for the elastic scattering of compound
particles by nuclei. The potentials used in optical model
analyses of the angular distributions are central, and apart from
energy and mass number, are functions only of the distance
between the centers of mass of the target and incident nuclei.
Thus, the radial size of the incident nucleus does not appear
explicitly but is included in the parameters of the potential.
The compound particles for which the angular distributions have
been measured are H^2, He^3, He^4, and N^{14}. For each compound
particle, the optical model has successfully fitted the elastic
scattering angular distributions. These analyses show that the
mean free path of a compound particle in nuclear matter is
small.

We shall first consider He^3. Hodgson (1960) finds that the
best-fit potentials for the scattering of 29 Mev He^3 by medium
nuclei have imaginary parts of from 15 to 30 Mev, equivalent
to mean free paths of only 1 to 2×10^{-13} cm. At lower energies,
owing to the charge of He^3, the Coulomb amplitude is greater
than the nuclear amplitude for most centre of mass angles.
However, Hodgson (1961b) has shown that there exists an
energy region where the elastic scattering depends mainly on the
diffuseness of the nuclear surface. The most useful energy is
of the order of $ZZ'/A^{1/3}$ Mev.

Hodgson (1960),[4] in considering the elastic scattering of 29 Mev He^3 by nickel, palladium, cadmium, and tin, has shown that the diffuseness parameter a_1 varies significantly with the target mass number. The absolute values of r_1 and a_1 depend on the sizes of both the He^3 and the target nucleus, and therefore both parameters have values greater than those found for the scattering of neutrons and protons. Thus Hodgson finds that r_1, for the best-fit potentials, is 1.6×10^{-13} cm. For 29 Mev He^3, Hodgson (1960) has shown that the diffuseness parameter a_1 can be very accurately determined by fitting the angular distribution with a volume absorption potential, to a centre of mass angle of about 50°. The values found (in units of 10^{-13} cm) are 0.61 ± 0.02 for nickel and palladium, 0.52 ± 0.03 for cadmium, and 0.50 ± 0.02 for tin. Possible reasons for these differences are shell structure and nuclear deformation.

A volume absorption optical model analysis of the scattering of 19 Mev H^2 by krypton and xenon has been made by England, McKeague, and Hodgson (1960). The imaginary parts of the best-fit potentials are 15 and 13 Mev, respectively, twice as great as the imaginary parts for protons of energy such that the velocity relative to the target is the same (see Table 1 of Section 3.3). For references to earlier work we refer to the paper of England et al.

Optical model analyses of the scattering of He^4 show that the mean free path in nuclear matter is short, as in the case of He^3. Igo (1958) found that the analysis determined the potential in the surface region but not in the interior of the target nucleus. References to earlier work are contained in Igo's paper.

An interesting extension of the analyses described has been made possible by the beams of heavy ions which now exist. The first application of the optical model to the elastic scattering of heavy ions was made by Porter (1958). For the scattering of N^{14} by N^{14}, Porter found that only the potential at large impact parameters could be determined. Bassel and Drisko (1960) analysed the scattering of 27 Mev N^{14} ions by Be^9.

---

[4] See also Greenlees, Lilley, Rowe, and Hodgson (1961); Aguilar, Garcia, England, Hodgson, and Toner (1961).

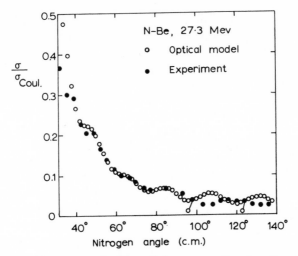

Fig. 10. The measured differential cross section for the elastic scattering of N^{14} by Be^9, divided by the cross section for Coulomb scattering, is compared with the prediction of a surface absorption optical model having the parameters $U_c = -50$, $W_c = 16$, $r_1 = r_2 = 1.23$, $a_1 = 0.65$, $a_0 = 1.125$, in units of Mev and of 10^{-13} cm (from Proc. of the International Conference on Nuclear Structure, Kingston, University of Toronto Press, 1960, p. 214).

The fit obtained from a surface absorption potential is shown in Figure 10. The experimental measurements are those of Halbert and Zucker (1959). A surface absorption optical model would not include the effect of elastic scattering of the heavy ions through Coulomb excited intermediate states.

Bromley, Kuehner, and Almqvist (1960) have measured the differential cross sections for C^{12}–C^{12} and O^{16}–O^{16} scattering as functions of energy for several fixed angles. The measurements of C^{12}–C^{12} scattering in the laboratory energy interval of from 6 to 29 Mev showed some evidence both for broad optical model resonances and for more narrow resonances which would be high spin excited states of Mg^{24}. For further information, we refer to the paper of Bromley et al. and to the papers of Vogt and McManus (1960) and Davis (1960).

The potentials for compound particles at the centre of the

target nucleus are not well determined because owing to the short mean free path, the scattering depends almost entirely on the potential in the nuclear surface. Experimental measurements of the reaction cross section and polarisation for compound particles are difficult but would be of value. For particles of unit spin, the most general form of the single-particle spin-orbit potential has been determined by Satchler (1960).

3.5 Mesons; the Exclusion Principle

Experimental measurements of the elastic scattering angular distributions and the reaction cross sections exist for K and π mesons. The problem is the determination of the sign of the real part of the meson-nucleus potential by measurement of the elastic scattering in the Coulomb interference region. These signs have now been determined for all possible cases. Moreover, the parameters of the best-fit potential for negative K-mesons are consistent with the ideas about the importance of the Pauli exclusion principle described in Sections 1.1 and 3.3.

The measurements of the K-meson elastic scattering were made by the nuclear photographic plate method. The problems which occur owing to the two groups of light and heavy target nuclei contained in the photographic plates are discussed in the paper of Melkanoff, Price, Stork, and Ticho (1959).

The Born approximation expansion 1.3-08 shows that only the volume integral and second moment of the potential are important in the Coulomb interference region, the momentum transfer being of the order of 50 Mev/c. Optical model analyses of K-meson scattering have therefore used Woods-Saxon volume absorption potentials which are central and have equal form factors b_1 and b_2. The fitting procedure starts from sets of parameters U_c, W_c, r_1, and a_1, which predict the experimental reaction cross section. Solutions of the Klein-Gordon equation are obtained by the method outlined in Section 1.4.

Determinations of the sign of U_c for negative K-mesons have been made by Melkanoff, Prowse, and Stork (1960) and by Jones (1960a). The experimental points of Melkanoff et al.

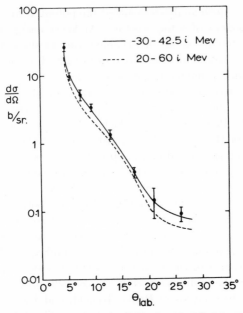

FIG. 11. The differential cross section for the elastic scattering of negative K-mesons by the nuclei of photographic plates is compared with the predictions of two volume absorption potentials, which both give the measured reaction cross section. The radial parameters are $r_1 = r_2 = 1.07$, and $a_1 = a_2 = 0.57$, in units of 10^{-13} cm (from Phys. Rev. Letters **4**, 183, 1960).

refer to the energy interval 95 to 125 Mev and are compared with two calculated angular distributions in Figure 11. The Coulomb interference region lies between 5° and 10°. The fitting procedure 3.3-01 shows that the sign of U_c is negative. The difference between the two distributions, which in the Born approximation is the Coulomb interference 1.3-18, is small owing to the large values of W_c. For potentials having the same form factor as the nuclear charge distribution, the results of both analyses show that U_c is about -30 Mev. The problem of the Lorentz transformation properties of the optical model potential is not important for K-meson kinetic energies of about

100 Mev. Both analyses assumed the potential to be the time-like component of a four-vector. At lower energies, the Coulomb interference is not observable owing to the large value of W_c. This large value, of the order of 50 Mev, occurs because the exclusion principle is not applicable.

The most recent and complete analysis of the elastic scattering and reaction cross sections of positive K-mesons is that of Melkanoff, Price, Stork, and Ticho (1959) at 125 Mev. The real part of the potential is repulsive, and of about 20 Mev.

The volume integral of the optical model potential provides a determination, through the impulse approximation equation 2.3-12, of the meson-nucleon forward scattering amplitude. However, at energies of the order of 100 Mev, both s- and p-wave meson-nucleon phase shifts must be considered, and there are six of these, taking into account isotopic spin dependence. For negative K-mesons, they must also be complex.

The real part of the π^- meson potential is attractive at energies below the first resonance in the π-nucleon system (see, for example, the analysis of Baker, Byfield, and Rainwater, 1958, who also give references to earlier work). The differential cross section measurements have been made at large angles and are therefore dependent on many moments of the optical model potential.

Thus, at 80 Mev, Baker et al. were unable to fit the angular distributions for lithium, carbon, aluminium, and copper with a potential proportional to the nuclear density distribution. The approximate equation 2.3-15 is unsatisfactory. The point at which the argument leading to 2.3-15 breaks down is the approximation of assuming that the transition amplitude is independent of the momentum transfer. This is not true for the π-nucleon system. A useful approximation, at energies substantially below the first resonance, is

$$\langle \mathbf{k}' \mid t_0 \mid \mathbf{k} \rangle = a + b\mathbf{k}_c' \cdot \mathbf{k}_c \left(\frac{\hbar}{m_\pi c} \right)^2$$

$$= a + \left(bk_c^2 - \frac{1}{2} bq^2 \right) \left(\frac{\hbar}{m_\pi c} \right)^2, \quad (3.5\text{-}01)$$

where a and b are constants, but depend on the isotopic spin state. The Compton wavelength of the π-meson is a convenient scaling factor, $\mathbf{k}_c$ and $\mathbf{k}_c'$ are the initial and final momenta in the π-nucleon centre of mass system, and q is the momentum transfer. Baker et al. show that 3.5-01 leads to a nonproportionality of potential and nuclear density. The potential can be found by substituting 3.5-01 in equation 2.3-13, which gives a form different in appearance from that found by Baker et al. We have,

$$
\begin{aligned}
U(k, r) \;=\; & A \left\{ a + \left(\frac{\hbar}{m_\pi c} \right)^2 b k_c^2 \right\} \rho(r) \\
& - \frac{Ab}{2(2\pi)^3} \left(\frac{\hbar}{m_\pi c} \right)^2 \int d\mathbf{q}\, q^2 F(q) e^{i\mathbf{q} \cdot \mathbf{r}} \\
=\; & A \left\{ a + \left(\frac{\hbar}{m_\pi c} \right)^2 b k_c^2 \right\} \rho(r) \\
& + \frac{1}{2} Ab \left(\frac{\hbar}{m_\pi c} \right)^2 \nabla^2 \rho(r).
\end{aligned}
\tag{3.5-02}
$$

For the π-nucleon system, $b \gg a$ and the second term in 3.5-02 is therefore considerable. For 80 Mev π^- mesons, Baker et al. show that such deviations from the nuclear density distribution are important for momentum transfers of 150 Mev/c or greater. The experimental angular distributions (Baker, Rainwater, and Williams, 1958) are well fitted by the modified potential.

APPENDIX A

Nonlocal Potential Models

A derivation of the momentum-dependent potentials equivalent to a class of separable nonlocal potentials has been given by F. G. J. Perey and B. Buck (1962). Consider first of all an infinite nucleus represented by a real nonlocal potential.

From 2.8-03, the Schrödinger equation, for a separable potential, is

$$-\frac{1}{2M}\,\nabla^2\psi(\mathbf{r}) + \int d\mathbf{x}\,U(E)u(x)\psi(\mathbf{r}+\mathbf{x}) = E\psi(\mathbf{r}), \quad (1)$$

where the function $u(x)$ is normalised,

$$\int d\mathbf{x}\,u(x) = 1. \tag{2}$$

For an infinite homogeneous potential,

$$\psi(\mathbf{r}+\mathbf{x}) = e^{i\mathbf{k}\cdot(\mathbf{r}+\mathbf{x})}, \tag{3}$$

where $\mathbf{k}$ is the momentum of the particle. Thus,

$$\frac{k^2}{2M} + \int d\mathbf{x}\,U(E)u(x)\,e^{i\mathbf{k}\cdot\mathbf{x}} = E. \tag{4}$$

It is then possible to carry out the integration over $\mathbf{x}$ by expanding $\sin kx$ in powers of kx, and the first two terms in the series, as shown in Section 2.8, would give the effective mass approximation. The inequality (2.8-10) necessary for the useful convergence of the series is not well satisfied. Therefore, Perey and Buck assumed $u(x)$ to be a gaussian,

$$u(x) = \frac{1}{\beta^3\pi\sqrt{\pi}}\,e^{-x^2/\beta^2}, \tag{5}$$

and performed the integration over $\mathbf{x}$ directly. Thus,

$$\frac{k^2}{2M} + U(E)e^{-(1/4)\beta^2 k^2} = E. \tag{6}$$

The local potential which gives the same dispersion law for the propagation of the nucleon in the medium,

$$\frac{k^2}{2M} + U_L(E,k^2) = E, \tag{7}$$

is therefore given by the equation,

$$U_L = Ue^{-(1/2)M\beta^2(E-U_L)} \tag{8}$$

The extension to complex potentials is direct, and if β_1 and β_2 are the range parameters of the nonlocalities in the real and imaginary parts, we have,

$$U_L - iW_L = U \exp\{-\tfrac{1}{2} M\beta_1^2(E - U_L + iW_L)\}$$
$$-iW \exp\{-\tfrac{1}{2} M\beta_2^2(E - U_L + iW_L)\}. \quad (9)$$

For a finite target nucleus, U and W are also functions of a coordinate $\mathbf{r}$. The extension to finite nuclei by Perey and Buck makes use of an approximation similar to the Thomas-Fermi approximation described in Section 3.3. It is assumed that the equivalent local potential at a point $\mathbf{r}$ is equal to the equivalent local potential for an infinite homogeneous medium for which the nonlocal potential is numerically equal to

$$U(E, \mathbf{r})u(x) - iW(E, \mathbf{r})w(x). \quad (10)$$

Then for a finite nucleus,

$$U_L(\mathbf{r}) - iW_L(\mathbf{r}) \approx U(\mathbf{r})e^{-(1/2)M\beta_1^2 E'} - iW(\mathbf{r})e^{-(1/2)M\beta_2^2 E'}, \quad (11)$$

where

$$E' = E - U_L(\mathbf{r}) + iW_L(\mathbf{r}). \quad (12)$$

Perey and Buck assumed the nonlocal potential to be independent of E and chose $\beta_1 = \beta_2 = \beta$. To find β, they used a local surface absorption optical model to fit the differential cross sections for the scattering of 7 and 14 Mev neutrons by Pb^{208}. From equation (11) and the two sets of local parameters they found $\beta = 0.88 \times 10^{-13}$ cm.

Perey and Buck have shown that equation (11) is accurate and have used it to estimate the compound elastic scattering cross section by the method described in Subsection 3.1.3.

There is no reason to believe that β_1 equals β_2 or that U and W are independent of E, and analyses without these restrictions would be of interest.

It is possible that the class of separable potentials 3.1-06 is not a good representation of the correct nonlocality and energy-dependence. For details of a simple model in which the forms of $u(x)$ and $w(x)$ are both different and energy-dependent, see Jones (1960b).

APPENDIX B

Antisymmetrization of the Incident Nucleon

In order to define the optical model potential for a nucleon, taking into account exchange processes, let us suppose, for simplicity, that the number of nucleons in the target is so large that the unperturbed states of the whole system can be approximated by antisymmetrized products of plane waves. The unperturbed state of a single nucleon is labelled by its momentum $\mathbf{k}'$ and by the spin and isotopic spin, which are denoted by s'. The greatest value of $\mathbf{k}'$ which occurs in the unperturbed ground state of the target is equal to the Fermi momentum k_F. The unperturbed Hamiltonian for the whole system is therefore

$$H_0 = \sum \{ U(k', s') + K(k', s') \} \tag{1}$$

where K and U are the single-particle kinetic and potential energy operators, and the summation is over the incident nucleon and the A nucleons in the target. The problem is to obtain the potential $U(k,s)$ for the incident nucleon by an extension of the Brueckner model (see, for example, Thouless, 1961, pp. 50–55). The potential is

$$U(k, s) = \sum_{\mathbf{k}'} \{ \langle \mathbf{k}, s; \mathbf{k}', s' \mid \mathbf{K} \mid \mathbf{k}, s; \mathbf{k}', s' \rangle$$

$$- \langle \mathbf{k}, s; \mathbf{k}', s' \mid \mathbf{K} \mid \mathbf{k}', s'; \mathbf{k}, s \rangle \} \tag{2}$$

with the restriction $k' < k_F$, where the K-matrix is defined, in terms of the potential between two nucleons, by

$$\mathbf{K} = v + v \frac{Q}{E_0 - H_0} v + v \frac{Q}{E_0 - H_0} v \frac{Q}{E_0 - H_0} v + \cdots \tag{3}$$

the energy of the unperturbed system being equal to E_0.
Equation (2) and the series (3) represent a sequence of processes
in which the incident nucleon and a target nucleon make transi-
tions from a state $| \mathbf{k}, s; \mathbf{k}', s' \rangle$ to intermediate states

$$| \mathbf{k}'', s''; \mathbf{k}''', s''' \rangle$$

and then back again. The projection operator Q allows only
k'' and k''' which are greater than k_F, so that for $k < k_F$, the
energy denominators in (3) are always negative and non-zero.
For $k > k_F$, the Brueckner model has to be modified slightly
because there are very many intermediate states which have
the same energy as the initial state. The energy denominators
in (3) can vanish, and (2) and (3) are defined only for complex
values of E_0. Owing to this degeneracy, the single-particle
potential will be complex, and the real and imaginary parts
may be separated by replacing the summations over momenta
by integrations and then employing the identity 2.1-12. The
imaginary part of the potential as a function of the difference
between k and k_F has been estimated by Shaw (1959).

Graphs for the first three terms of the series (3) are shown in

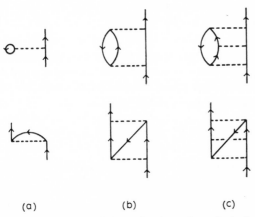

(a)   (b)   (c)

Fig. 12. The first three orders of the class of graphs included in the
K-matrix, defined for a nucleon in a state above the Fermi surface.
The lower three are the exchange graphs.

Figure 12. A line directed upwards represents an occupied state above the Fermi surface. Therefore, the lines entering and leaving the graphs represent the incident and scattered nucleons respectively. A line directed downwards represents the unoccupied state (or hole) below the Fermi surface which is created when a nucleon is excited. The horizontal broken lines represent the interactions v. For a complete account of the analysis of the Rayleigh-Schrödinger perturbation series by the method of graphs we refer to Thouless (1961, pp. 35–48).

Discussions of the optical model in which the incident nucleon is antisymmetrized with the target nucleons are contained in the papers of Brueckner, Eden, and Francis (1955), Bell and Squires (1959), and Shaw (1959).

The quantum mechanical identity of the incident and target nucleons contributes to the momentum dependence of the single-particle or optical model potential (Weisskopf, 1957). For nucleon-nucleon potentials for which the Fourier transform exists, this can be seen from the Hartree-Fock approximation, the graphs of Figure 12, part (a). With neglect of the spin variables,

$$U(k) \; = \; \rho v(0) \; - \; \frac{\rho}{A} \sum_{\mathbf{k}'} v(|\, \mathbf{k} \, - \, \mathbf{k}' \,|), \qquad (4)$$

for $|\, \mathbf{k}' \,| \; < \; k_F$, where ρ is the nucleon density, and $v(q)$ is the Fourier transform of the potential. The second term on the right-hand side of equation (4), the exchange term, is a function of the momentum of the incident nucleon, and tends to zero when this momentum becomes large.

References

Adair, R. K., *Phys. Rev.* **94**, 737 (1954).

Aguilar, J., A. Garcia, J. B. A. England, P. E. Hodgson, and W. T. Toner, *Nuclear Phys.* **25**, 259 (1961).

Albert, R. D., and L. F. Hansen, *Phys. Rev.* **123**, 1749 (1961).

Baker, W. F., H. Byfield, and J. Rainwater, *Phys. Rev.* **112**, 1773 (1958).

Baker, W. F., J. Rainwater, and R. E. Williams, *Phys. Rev.* **112**, 1763 (1958).

Barschall, H. H., *Phys. Rev.* **86**, 431 (1952).

Bassel, R. H., and R. M. Drisko, *Proceedings of the International Conference on Nuclear Structure, Kingston* (University of Toronto Press, Toronto, 1960), p. 212.

Bell, J. S., and E. J. Squires, *Phys. Rev. Letters* **3**, 96 (1959).

Berg, R. A., and L. Wilets, *Phys. Rev.* **101**, 201 (1956).

Bethe, H. A., *Phys. Rev.* **47**, 747 (1935).

Bethe, H. A., *Phys. Rev.* **57**, 1125 (1940).

Bethe, H. A., *Ann. Phys.* **3**, 190 (1958).

Bethe, H. A., and J. Goldstone, *Proc. Roy. Soc. (London)* **A238**, 551 (1957).

Bjerge, T., and C. H. Westcott, *Proc. Roy. Soc. (London)* **A150**, 709 (1935).

Bjorklund, F., *Proceedings of the International Conference on the Nuclear Optical Model* (Florida State University Studies, No. 32, 1959), p. 1.

Bjorklund, F., and S. Fernbach, *Phys. Rev.* **109**, 1295 (1958).

Blatt, J. M., and V. F. Weisskopf, *Theoretical Nuclear Physics* (Wiley, New York, 1952).

Bloch, C., *Nuclear Phys.* **4**, 503 (1957).

Bohr, N., *Nature* **137**, 344 (1936).

Bowen, P. H., J. P. Scanlon, G. H. Stafford, J. J. Thresher, and P. E. Hodgson, *Nuclear Phys.* **22**, 640 (1961).

Breit, G., *Handbuch der Physik* (Springer-Verlag, Berlin, 1959) Vol. 41/1, p. 1.

Breit, G., and E. Wigner, *Phys. Rev.* **49**, 519 (1936).

Bromley, D. A., J. A. Kuehner, and E. Almqvist, *Phys. Rev. Letters* **4**, 365 (1960).

Brown, G. E., *Proc. Phys. Soc. (London)* **A70**, 681 (1957).

112 OPTICAL MODEL IN NUCLEAR AND PARTICLE PHYSICS

Brown, G. E., *Revs. Modern Phys.* **31**, 893 (1959).
Brown, G. E., *Proceedings of the International Conference on Nuclear Structure, Kingston* (University of Toronto Press, Toronto, 1960), p. 135.
Brown, G. E., and C. T. De Dominicis, *Proc. Phys. Soc. (London)* **A72**, 70 (1958).
Brown, G. E., C. T. De Dominicis, and J. S. Langer, *Ann. Phys.* **6**, 209 (1959).
Brueckner, K. A., *Phys. Rev.* **97**, 1353 (1955).
Brueckner, K. A., *Phys. Rev.* **103**, 1121 (1956).
Brueckner, K. A., R. J. Eden, and N. C. Francis, *Phys. Rev.* **100**, 891 (1955).
Brueckner, K. A., J. L. Gammel, and H. Weitzner, *Phys. Rev.* **110**, 431 (1958).
Buck, B., R. N. Maddison, and P. E. Hodgson, *Phil. Mag.* **5**, 1181 (1960).
Campbell, E. J., H. Feshbach, C. E. Porter, and V. F. Weisskopf, *Technical Report* No. 73 (Massachusetts Institute of Technology, Laboratory for Nuclear Science, 1960).
Chase, D. M., and F. Rohrlich, *Phys. Rev.* **94**, 81 (1954).
Chase, D. M., L. Wilets, and A. R. Edmonds, *Phys. Rev.* **110**, 1080 (1958).
Chew, G. F., and M. L. Goldberger, *Phys. Rev.* **87**, 778 (1952).
Chew, G. F., and G. C. Wick, *Phys. Rev.* **85**, 636 (1952).
Courant, R., and D. Hilbert, *Methods of Mathematical Physics* (Interscience, New York, 1953), Vol. 1.
Cromer, A. H., *Phys. Rev.* **113**, 1607 (1959).
Davies, H., *Nuclear Phys.* **14**, 465 (1960).
Davis, R. H., *Phys. Rev. Letters* **4**, 521 (1960).
Dirac, P. A. M., *The Principles of Quantum Mechanics* (Oxford University Press, 1947).
Edmonds, A. R., *Angular Momentum in Quantum Mechanics* (Princeton University Press, 1957).
Eisberg, R. M., D. R. Yennie, and D. H. Wilkinson, *Nuclear Phys.* **18**, 338 (1960).
Elliot, J. P., and A. M. Lane, *Handbuch der Physik* (Springer-Verlag, Berlin, 1957) Vol. 39, p. 241.
England, J. B. A., R. McKeague, and P. E. Hodgson, *Nuclear Phys.* **16**, 52 (1960).
Fermi, E., *Nuovo cimento* **11**, 407 (1954).
Fernbach, S., R. Serber, and T. B. Taylor, *Phys. Rev.* **75**, 1352 (1949).
Feshbach, H., *Ann. Phys.* **5**, 357 (1958a).
Feshbach, H., *Ann. Rev. Nuclear Sci.* **8**, 49 (1958b).
Feshbach, H., C. E. Porter, and V. F. Weisskopf, *Phys. Rev.* **96**, 448 (1954).

Ford, K. W., and D. Bohm, *Phys. Rev.* **79,** 745 (1950).

Fox, L., and E. T. Goodwin, *Phil. Trans. Roy Soc. London* **A245,** 501 (1953).

Frahn, W. E., and R. H. Lemmer, *Nuovo cimento* **6,** 664 (1957).

Friedman, F. L., and V. F. Weisskopf, *Niels Bohr and the Development of Physics* (Pergamon, London, 1955), p. 134.

Gammel, J. L., and R. M. Thaler, *Phys. Rev.* **107,** 291, 1337 (1957).

Gammel, J. L., and R. M. Thaler, *Phys. Rev.* **109,** 2041 (1958).

Gell-Mann, M., and M. L. Goldberger, *Phys. Rev.* **91,** 398 (1953).

Glassgold, A. E., and P. J. Kellog, *Phys. Rev.* **107,** 1372 (1957).

Gomes, L. C., *Phys. Rev.* **116,** 1226 (1959).

Green, A. E. S., and P. C. Sood, *Phys. Rev.* **111,** 1147 (1958).

Greenlees, G. W., and O. N. Jarvis, *Proceedings of the International Conference on Nuclear Structure, Kingston* (University of Toronto Press, Toronto, 1960), p. 217.

Greenlees, G. W., J. S. Lilley, P. C. Rowe, and P. E. Hodgson, *Nuclear Phys.* **24,** 334 (1961).

Gugelot, P. C., *Proceedings of the International Conference on Nuclear Structure, Kingston* (University of Toronto Press, Toronto, 1960), p. 157.

Halbert, M. L., and A. Zucker, *Phys. Rev.* **115,** 1635 (1959).

Hamilton, J., *The Theory of Elementary Particles* (Oxford University Press, 1959).

Harada, K., and N. Oda, *Progr. Theoret. Phys. (Kyoto)* **21,** 260 (1959).

Heckrotte, W., *Phys. Rev.* **101,** 1406 (1956).

Hodgson, P. E., *Nuclear Phys.* **21,** 28 (1960).

Hodgson, P. E., *Phys. Rev. Letters* **6,** 358 (1961a).

Hodgson, P. E., *Nuclear Phys.* **23,** 499 (1961b).

Hofstadter, R., *Ann. Rev. Nuclear Sci.* **7,** 231 (1957).

Hughes, D. J., R. L. Zimmerman, and R. E. Chrien, *Phys. Rev. Letters* **1,** 461 (1958).

Humblet, J., and L. Rosenfeld, *Nuclear Phys.* **26,** 529 (1961).

Igo, G., *Phys. Rev. Letters* **1,** 72 (1958).

Jancovici, B., *Nuclear Phys.* **21,** 256 (1960).

Johansson, A., U. Svanberg, and P. E. Hodgson, *Arkiv Fysik* **19,** 541 (1961).

Jones, P. B., *Proc. Roy. Soc. (London)* **A257,** 109 (1960a), and **A255,** 253 (1960b).

Kapur, P. L., and R. E. Peierls, *Proc. Roy. Soc. (London)* **A166,** 277 (1938).

Kerman, A. K., H. McManus, and R. M. Thaler, *Ann. Phys.* **8,** 551 (1959).

Kikuchi, K., *Nuclear Phys.* **12,** 305 (1959).

Köhler, H. S., *Nuclear Phys.* **1**, 433 (1956).

Krueger, T. K., and B. Margolis, *Nuclear Phys.* **28**, 578 (1961).

Landau, L. D., and E. M. Lifshitz, *Quantum Mechanics—Non-Relativistic Theory* (Pergamon, London, 1958).

Lane, A. M., *Nuclear Phys.* **35**, 676 (1962).

Lane, A. M., *Revs. Modern Phys.* **29**, 191 (1957).

Lane, A. M., J. E. Lynn, E. Melkonian, and E. R. Rae, *Phys. Rev. Letters* **2**, 424 (1959).

Lane, A. M., R. G. Thomas, and E. P. Wigner, *Phys. Rev.* **98**, 693 (1955).

Lane, A. M., and R. G. Thomas, *Revs. Modern Phys.* **30**, 257 (1958).

Lane, A. M., and C. F. Wandel, *Phys. Rev.* **98**, 1524 (1955).

Lemmer, R. H., Th. A. J. Maris, and Y. C. Tang, *Nuclear Phys.* **12**, 619 (1959).

Levinson, H., *Kgl. Danske Videnskab. Selskab, Mat.-fys. Medd.* **25**, No. 9 (1949).

Lippmann, B. A., M. H. Mittleman, and K. M. Watson, *Phys. Rev.* **116**, 920 (1959).

Lippman, B., and J. Schwinger, *Phys. Rev.* **79**, 469 (1950).

Margolis, B., *Proceedings of the International Conference on the Nuclear Optical Model* (Florida State University Studies, No. 32, 1959), p. 34.

Martin, A., *Nuovo cimento* **14**, 403 (1959).

McManus, H., and R. M. Thaler, *Phys. Rev.* **110**, 590 (1958).

Melkanoff, M. A., J. S. Nodvik, D. S. Saxon, and R. D. Woods, *Phys. Rev.* **106**, 793 (1957).

Melkanoff, M. A., O. R. Price, D. H. Stork, and H. K. Ticho, *Phys. Rev.* **113**, 1303 (1959).

Melkanoff, M. A., D. J. Prowse, and D. H. Stork, *Phys. Rev. Letters* **4**, 183 (1960).

Meyer, V., and N. M. Hintz, *Phys. Rev. Letters* **5**, 207 (1960).

Miller, D. W., R. K. Adair, C. K. Bockelman, and S. E. Darden, *Phys. Rev.* **88**, 83 (1952).

Mittleman, M. H., and K. M. Watson, *Phys. Rev.* **113**, 198 (1959).

Møller, C., *Kgl. Danske Videnskab. Selskab. Mat.-fys. Medd.* **23**, No. 1 (1945).

Moon, P. B., and J. R. Tillman, *Nature* **135**, 904 (1935).

Moszkowski, S. A., *Handbuch der Physik* (Springer-Verlag, Berlin, 1957) Vol. 39, p. 411.

Mott, N. F., and H. S. W. Massey, *The Theory of Atomic Collisions* (Oxford University Press, 1949).

Nodvik, J. S., and D. S. Saxon, *Phys. Rev.* **117**, 1539 (1960).

Peierls, R. E., *Proc. Cambridge Phil. Soc.* **44**, 242 (1948).

Perey, F. G. J., and B. Buck, *Nuclear Phys.* **32**, 353 (1962).

Porter, C. E., *Phys. Rev.* **112**, 1722 (1958).

Ravenhall, D. G., *Revs. Modern Phys.* **30,** 430 (1958).

Rosen, L., *Proceedings of the International Conference on Nuclear Structure, Kingston* (University of Toronto Press, Toronto, 1960), p. 185.

Rosen, L., J. E. Brolley Jr., and L. Stewart, *Phys. Rev.* **121,** 1423 (1961).

Rosenfeld, L., *Nuclear Phys.* **26,** 579 (1961).

Ross, A. A., H. Mark, and R. D. Lawson, *Phys. Rev.* **102,** 1613 (1956).

Satchler, G. R., *Phys. Rev.* **109,** 429 (1958).

Satchler, G. R., *Nuclear Phys.* **21,** 116 (1960).

Sawicki, J., and S. A. Moszkowski, *Nuclear Phys.* **21,** 456 (1960).

Schiffer, J. P., *Proceedings of the International Conference on Nuclear Structure, Kingston* (University of Toronto Press, Toronto, 1960), p. 676.

Schweber, S. S., H. A. Bethe, and F. de Hoffmann, *Mesons and Fields* (Row, Peterson & Co., New York, 1955) Vol. 1.

Schwinger, J., *Phys. Rev.* **73,** 407 (1948).

Scott, J. M. C., *Phil. Mag.* **45,** 1322 (1954).

Serber, R., *Phys. Rev.* **72,** 1114 (1947).

Seth, K. K., *Revs. Modern Phys.* **30,** 442 (1958).

Seth, K. K., D. J. Hughes, R. L. Zimmerman, and R. C. Garth, *Phys. Rev.* **110,** 692 (1958).

Shaw, G. L., *Ann. Phys.* **8,** 509 (1959).

Siegert, A. J. F., *Phys. Rev.* **56,** 750 (1939).

Stapp, H. P., T. J. Ypsilantis, and N. Metropolis, *Phys. Rev.* **105,** 302 (1957).

Sugie, A., *Phys. Rev. Letters* **4,** 286 (1960).

Szilard, L., *Nature* **136,** 950 (1935).

Temmer, G. M., *Revs. Modern Phys.* **30,** 498 (1958).

Thouless, D. J., *The Quantum Mechanics of Many-Body Systems* (Academic Press, New York, 1961).

Titchmarsh, E. C., *The Theory of Functions* (Oxford University Press, 1939), 2nd edition.

Vogt, E., and H. McManus, *Phys. Rev. Letters* **4,** 518 (1960).

Voss, R. G. P., and R. Wilson, *Phil. Mag.* **1,** 175 (1956).

Walt, M., *Proceedings of the International Conference on Nuclear Structure, Kingston* (University of Toronto Press, Toronto, 1960), p. 146.

Watson, K. M., *Phys. Rev.* **105,** 1388 (1957).

Watson, K. M., *Revs. Modern Phys.* **30,** 565 (1958).

Weisskopf, V. F., *Science* **113,** 101 (1951).

Weisskopf, V. F., *Nuclear Phys.* **3,** 423 (1957).

Wigner, E. P., *Science* **120,** 790 (1954).

Wigner, E. P., and L. Eisenbud, *Phys. Rev.* **72,** 29 (1947).

Wilson, R., *Phys. Rev.* **114,** 260 (1959).

Wolfenstein, L., *Ann. Rev. Nuclear Sci.* **6,** 43 (1956).

Woods, R. D., and D. S. Saxon, *Phys. Rev.* **95,** 577 (1954).

Index

116